Doctors in the Medicinal Garden
Plants named after physicians

Doctors in the
Medicinal Garden
Plants named
after physicians

Dr Henry Oakeley FRCP FLS

Citation for this book: Oakeley HF. *Doctors in the Medicinal Garden. Plants named after physicians*. London: Royal College of Physicians, 2012.

ISBN: 978-1-86016-468-2 (paperback)
ISBN: 978-1-86016-491-0 (hardback)

Royal College of Physicians
11 St Andrews Place
Regent's Park
London NW1 4LE

www.rcplondon.ac.uk
www.oakeleybooks.com

Registered Charity No 210508

Further copies of this book are available to order from: www.rcplondon.ac.uk

British Library Cataloguing in Publication Data:
A catalogue record of this book is available from the British Library.

Medical text reviewer: Dr Anthony Dayan, FRCP
Horticultural information: Clare Beacham, RCP gardener
Production editor: Urooj Asif Akhtar, RCP Corporate Communications and Publishing team
Designer: James Partridge, RCP Corporate Communications and Publishing team

Images: Plants in the Medicinal Garden © Dr Henry Francis Oakeley and
the Royal College of Physicians.
Other images: © Dr Henry Francis Oakeley unless otherwise specified.
Specified images: © the Royal College of Physicians; © the Wellcome Library, London;
© the director and trustees of the Royal Botanic Gardens, Kew; and others as indicated.

Printed in Malta by Gutenberg Press.

Acknowledgements

For translation of texts from Swedish, I am grateful to Inger Borg and Toby Lowsley-Williams, from German to Stephanie Ellrott and Guido Braem, from Spanish to Mónica Castedo-López, and from Japanese to Mayumi Hashi. I am grateful also to Manolo Arias for identifying a Peruvian herb, and to the trustees of the Natal Society Foundation and Peter Croeser for the images of Dr Peter Cormack Sutherland and *Greyia sutherlandia*. The help from the staff of the Lindley Library at the Royal Horticultural Society; from Peter Basham, Sarah Gillam and Sarah Burnett at the Royal College of Physicians; Julia Buckley at the Library of the Royal Botanic Gardens, Kew, and Catherine Draycott and Emily Doyle at the Wellcome Library with research, sourcing of images and photography is much appreciated. The advice of Dr Anthony Dayan FRCP in the preparation of this book has been invaluable.

I am especially grateful to Clare Beacham, gardener to the Royal College of Physicians, for the horticultural information on the plants; Urooj Akhtar, Orla Fee, Suzanne Fuzzey, James Partridge and Joanna Reid from the Corporate Communications and Publishing team for all their hard work and support in producing this book.

Images from the Royal Botanic Gardens, Kew, are reproduced with the kind permission of the director and the board of trustees. Images from the Wellcome Library are reproduced with the kind permission of the Wellcome Library, London.

Contents

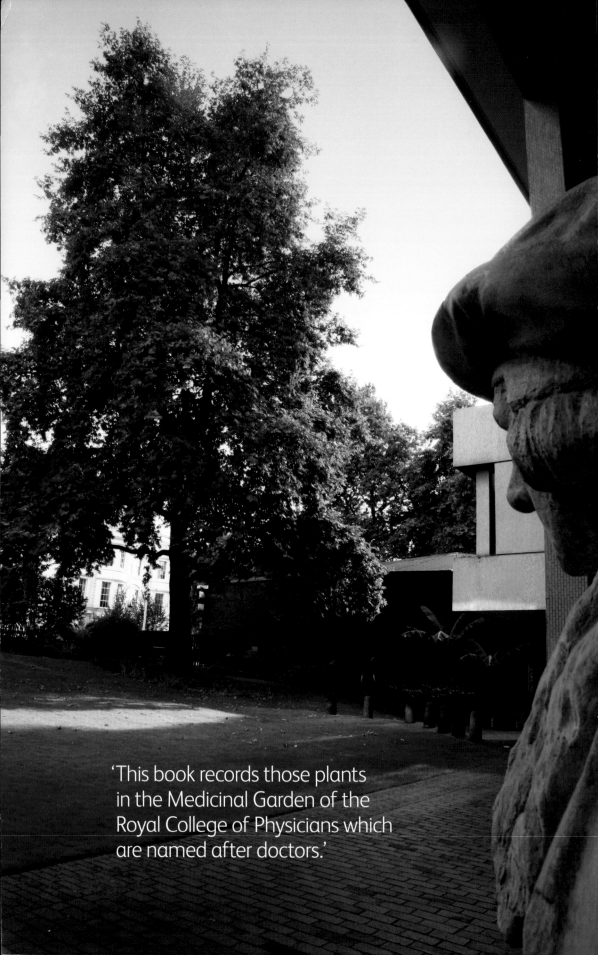

'This book records those plants
in the Medicinal Garden of the
Royal College of Physicians which
are named after doctors.'

Preface

The more one knows about a plant, its history, its naming, its cultivation and its uses, the more interesting it becomes. This book records those plants in the Medicinal Garden of the Royal College of Physicians which are named after doctors and apothecaries (including a Jesuit missionary who ran a pharmacy), a few gods (medical ones), at least one doctor of divinity, a failed medical student and two kings with medicinal interests. A botanist with strong medical links has been included, as has the gardener Joseph Dieffenbach, who is often supplanted in etymological dictionaries by two medical doctors with the same surname.

In the year 2011, the Medicinal Garden contained 1,300 different plants which are either used, or have been used, in medicine during past millennia or which commemorate physicians. Many are of no medicinal use, but, like the ancient books in the Royal College of Physicians library, record the beliefs and practices of past ages and cultures. This is not a garden set out to be merely decorative; its fascination lies in its plants, their uses and dangers, the history and the folklore surrounding them, and even in their names and the influence they have had on the English language. In the words of a visitor on one of the regularly conducted tours, 'it is the most interesting garden in London'.

Memorial immortality is conferred by having a plant named after one, although, as Hippocrates demonstrates, an oath may be better. The Medicinal Garden commemorates both the medicines and the physicians of bygone ages, but as knowledge of plants dwindles in the face of the relentless onslaught of the electronic age, so does our remembrance of our forefathers. The lives and contributions of many whose names live on in plant names have been forgotten. I hope this book will help retrieve them from obscurity and be a useful reference for those who enjoy the historical aspects of gardening as well the pleasures of horticulture. A few reminders of the medicinal and other uses of their plants are included.

The Medicinal Garden is cared for by Jane Knowles, head gardener, and Clare Beacham (who contributed the horticultural information). We are all grateful to them.

Dr Henry Oakeley, FRCP FLS
The Garden Fellow, Royal College of Physicians
April 2012

Opposite page: Thomas Linacre (1460–1524), first president of the Royal College of Physicians, looks out over the Medicinal Garden.

Abelia x grandiflora

Abelia x *grandiflora* Clarke Abel

The name celebrates the short life of Dr Clarke Abel MD FRS (1789–1826), one of the first European botanists to collect in China, which he did when attached as physician to the Canton Embassy in 1816–17.

Dr Clarke Abel MD FRS (1789–1826)
Image: © Royal College of Physicians

On the recommendation of Sir Joseph Banks he accompanied the ambassador, Lord Amherst, doubling as the expedition botanist on a mission to meet the Emperor of China. As the delegation declared on arrival at the palace that they would not prostrate themselves (kow-tow), they were not allowed to meet him. So they returned to Canton, unescorted and with great difficulty and risk. Abel was not well during the journey, but his assistant, Hooper (a gardener from Kew), collected seed and herbarium material from 300 plants.

The whole collection was lost when HMS *Alceste*, the ship taking him home, was wrecked on a coral reef in the Banca Straits off the coast of Sumatra, and when the crew were attacked by Malay pirates upon reaching the shore. Abel wrote of his travels in a *Narrative of a journey in the interior of China* (1818) that 'after leaving the wreck of the *Alceste*, I had the mortification of hearing that the cases containing the seeds had been brought upon deck and emptied of their contents by one of the seamen, to make room for some of the linen of one of the gentlemen of the Embassy'. However, later he writes that the 'collection of plants, seeds and minerals which had been made in China, was still in a great measure, uninjured ... and by his [the commanding officer] directions was placed upon a raft, which, with everything upon it, was burnt by the Malays'. Some duplicates, including *Abelia chinensis* and *Prunus mume*, came back to England separately with Sir George Staunton, second-in-command at the Embassy (Cox, 1945). During his enforced stay in Sumatra, Abel discovered the orang-utan there. On his return to England, he was elected a fellow of the Royal Society (March 1819).

When Lord Amherst was appointed governor general of India, Abel accompanied him as surgeon-in-chief, but died there in 1826, aged 37.

Abelia x *grandiflora* is a hybrid between *A. chinensis* and *A. uniflora*. It has no medicinal use but is a popular ornamental shrub because it has a long flowering period. ∎

> **Abelia x grandiflora is a graceful, semi-evergreen shrub in the family Caprifoliaceae. It grows happily in a raised bed under a large plane tree, producing a profusion of small, fragrant, pink-flushed white flowers. We prune it in early spring to remove dead or damaged wood, and in autumn we remove old branches to maintain a balanced shape. Each year, a layer of well-rotted manure is applied around the base.**

Acanthus dioscoridis

Acanthus dioscoridis Pedanius Dioscorides

Woodcut of *Acanthus mollis* from Mattioli (1569)

ACANTHVS.

This spiny-leaved herbaceous plant was named for Pedanius Dioscorides of Anazarbus (AD *c.* 40–90), a Greek physician and herbalist who practised in Rome. He was born in Anazarbus, in the Roman province of Cicilia, during the reign of Tiberius or Caligula, and was a contemporary of Pliny the Younger (AD 61–112).

He studied pharmacology in Tarsus under the teacher Arius/Areios, to whom he dedicates his book, *De materia medica*. He lived 'a soldier's life' – viz an itinerant one – travelling through the Greek-speaking part of the Roman Empire, Sicily, southern Italy and possibly into Gaul. His book remained the main source of herbal medicinal information for the next 1,600 years. It was translated into Latin and Arabic, being copied by hand for 1,400 years. It had no illustrations and it is difficult to be certain what plants he was writing about. In 491 the *Vienna Dioscorides,* also known as the *Anicia Juliana codex*, was produced, a manuscript with paintings of what contemporary writers believed were the plants of Dioscorides. The next major attempt at establishing what they were came in the commentaries of Mattioli (1569) and Ruellio (1543), as well as the herbals of Fuchs (1542) and Dodoens (1554), all lavishly illustrated with woodcuts.

The genus *Acanthus* extends throughout Europe, to northern Africa and Asia. *Acanthus mollis,* known as Bear's Breeches or Brank Ursine and Bear's Foot, has naturalised itself in Britain, reputedly brought here by the Romans. Dioscorides may also be interpreted as saying that *A. mollis* is found in gardens and *A. spinosus* in the wild. >

> **Acanthus dioscoridis** in the family Acanthaceae is usually found on dry rocky hillsides in Iran, Iraq and southern Turkey. In the herbaceous border, spikes of pink hooded flowers in summer with silvery-green basal leaves are striking. It is fully hardy, but well-drained soil is essential as it does not cope well with wet soil in winter. Established plants can be divided in early autumn or spring to increase stocks.

'*Acanthus spinosus*, with its spiky, sharply divided leaves was copied as an ornament by the Greeks, originally in metal and then in stone on the tops of pillars.'

Pedanius Dioscorides of Anazarbus from Blackwell's *Curious herbal* (1737). Image: © Royal College of Physicians

Plant classification 2,000 years ago often gave separate names to the same plant depending on whether it was wild or cultivated, and interpreting the identity of Greek plant names from so long ago is often guesswork. *Acanthus spinosus*, with its spiky, sharply divided leaves was copied as an ornament by the Greeks, originally in metal and then in stone on the tops of pillars. *Acanthus mollis,* with its wider leaves and pan-Italian distribution, was used by the Romans for the same purpose – as capitals on Corinthian pillars.

Medicinally, from the time of Dioscorides (1st century AD) to Salmon (1710), herbalists recommended that the roots applied as a poultice were a cure for broken limbs, burns, numbness of the hands and feet, and for tuberculosis ('pthisis') and spitting blood. It has no current medicinal use. ∎

Acanthus.

Achillea clavennae Niccolò Chiavenna

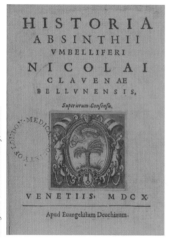

This yarrow commemorates Niccolò (also Nicolao) Chiavenna (Nicolaus Clavena, *d.* 1617), an Italian surgeon, botanist and apothecary from Belluno, at that time in the Republic of Venice.

He worked in the 'Bottega dei Rimedi Semplici', the shop for herbal remedies [simples], at the sign of the Angel, next to the church of Santo Stefano in Belluno. Here he prepared his medicine with a mortar, used an alembic for distillation, and worked among the great glass bottles which contained scents and medicines with the same care as he collected the herbs from their habitats in the valley of Belluno, about which he was reputed to be an expert. His favourite place was the mountain known as Monte Serva in the Dolomites, above the Col di Roanza to the north of Belluno. Here, on one of his innumerable excursions, he discovered a plant which had not been previously described. In order to claim priority in the discovery of what he called the 'umbilliferous absinthium', known locally as the Achillea of Monte Serva (now *Achillea clavennae*), he published *Historia absinthii umbelliferi* (1609). He extolled its virtues for stomach complaints and as an anti-helminthic. The bishop of Belluno, Aloisio Lollinio, publicly thanked him for curing his stomach problems with a medicine made from this herb. He made such a lot of money from it that he tried to obtain a monopoly licence to be its only purveyor, but came in for some criticism, notably from Pompeo Sprecchis (fl. 1611), a pharmacist from Venice, in *Antabsinthium Clavennae* (1609), which points out that the plant had already been described by L'Escluse (Carolus Clusius). However, he had posthumous recognition as the victor of the argument when Linnaeus named it for him.

'The bishop of Belluno, Aloisio Lollinio, publicly thanked him for curing his stomach problems with a medicine made from this herb.'

It is not a particularly common plant and does not appear in herbals, but it can still be found in the western Dolomites and in particular on Monte Serva.

In vitro testing of *Achillea clavennae* (Bezić N *et al*, 2003) shows that the essential oils extracted by distillation of the plant have antibacterial action against *Klebsiella pneumoniae* and *Pseudomonas aeruginosa* and fungal organisms in the laboratory, but this has no serious implications for potential use as an antibiotic for our diseases. >

Achillea clavennae

ABSINTHIVM
Vmbelli   ferum

Achillea clavennae

After all, there are lots of chemicals which one uses for cleaning kitchen surfaces which are advertised as killing '99% of all known germs', but one would not even consider drinking them. The chemicals which make up its essential oils are mostly camphor (which can cause convulsions, gastrointestinal irritation and possibly liver damage), linalool (used in scents and as an insecticide against fleas and cockroaches), beta-caryophyllene, a chemical abundant in *Cannabis* plants, but which has no psychomimetic effect (Gertsch, 2008), and myrcene, a chemical used as an intermediary in the perfumery industry. There is always a long road to travel to make antibiotics which work in a test tube safe for human consumption, and effective when ingested, from raw chemicals. ∎

'There are lots of chemicals which one uses for cleaning kitchen surfaces which are advertised as killing "99% of all known germs", but one would not even consider drinking them.'

This silvery-leaved perennial, in the Asteraceae family, hails from the mountainous regions of middle and south-eastern Europe. In the Medicinal Garden it thrives in a raised, well-drained, sunny border where it forms an attractive ground cover. It is fully hardy as long as the soil is free-draining as it will not tolerate winter wet. It can be propagated by division in spring.

Achillea millefolium

Achillea millefolium Achilles

Achillea millefolium from Ruellio (1543)

Not strictly a physician, but the Greek warrior Achilles used this plant for healing wounds – having been taught its properties by his teacher, Chiron the centaur.

Achilles is the hero of Homer's *Iliad* (*c.* 800 BC) despite his rather variable enthusiasm for the Trojan War, his complicated relationships and fiery temper. He was killed by Paris with an arrow, which hit his heel – the only part of his body which had not been made invulnerable when his mother had dipped him in the river Styx.

The plant is known as Yarrow or Sneezewort, the latter because *A. ptarmica*, dried and ground up, was used as an errhine – a snuff to induce sneezing. Dioscorides calls it Achilles' Woundwort, *sideritis*, writing that the ground-up foliage closes bleeding wounds, relieves inflammation and stops uterine bleeding. Johnson (1633) says that, put up one's nose, it causes a nosebleed and so stops migraines. Not a concept which is comprehensible today. ■

In the Asteraceae family, this hardy perennial grows naturally in grassy areas of Europe and west Asia. It has attractive, ferny foliage and white to pink flat flowers in summer and autumn. It will grow in any well-drained soil in the sun. Although drought tolerant, our plants can be prone to mildew if it gets very dry. Plants can be staked or cut back in May to produce stronger growth, with a later flowering period. It is easy to propagate from cuttings or by division in autumn.

Aconitum carmichaelii JR Carmichael

Engraving of *Aconitum napellus* from *Medical botany* (Anon, 1819–21)

Monkshood or Wolfsbane, with its dark blue flowers, is a plant for the herbaceous border and a source of the neurotoxin aconitine. Named for Dr JR Carmichael (*d.* 1877), English physician, plant collector and Protestant missionary in Guangdong and Shandong, China.

He arrived in Hong Kong on 14 February 1862, accompanied by Mrs Hill and the Rev Jonathon Lees and Mrs Lees. Initially (1862–3), he was in charge of the hospital of the London Missionary Society in Canton. He then went into private medical practice in Che Foo (now called Yantai, in Shandong province) in northern China. He married the eldest sister of the American botanist and opium trader, Francis Blackwell Forbes, and assisted in the latter's botanical collections at Che Foo in 1874 on behalf of the Royal Botanic Gardens, Kew. He died of 'famine fever', caught from his patients in the hospital he set up to deal with the great famine in northern China in 1877 (Bretschneider, 1898).

The sap of *A. carmichaelii* was used in China as an arrow poison (Bisset NG, 1981), but its European counterpart, *A. napellus*, is equally poisonous and was used to kill wolves and dogs. It was well known to the physicians of the early 19th century. Lindley (1838) describes how three out of five people who drank alcohol to which the leaves of *A. napellus* had been added, having mistaken it for Lovage (*Levisticum officinale*), died within three hours of 'vomiting, purging, burning in the throat, colic and swelling in the belly'. >

'The sap of *Aconitum carmichaelii* was used in China as an arrow poison (Bisset NG, 1981), but its European counterpart, *A. napellus*, is equally poisonous and was used to kill wolves and dogs.'

Doctors in the Medicinal Garden

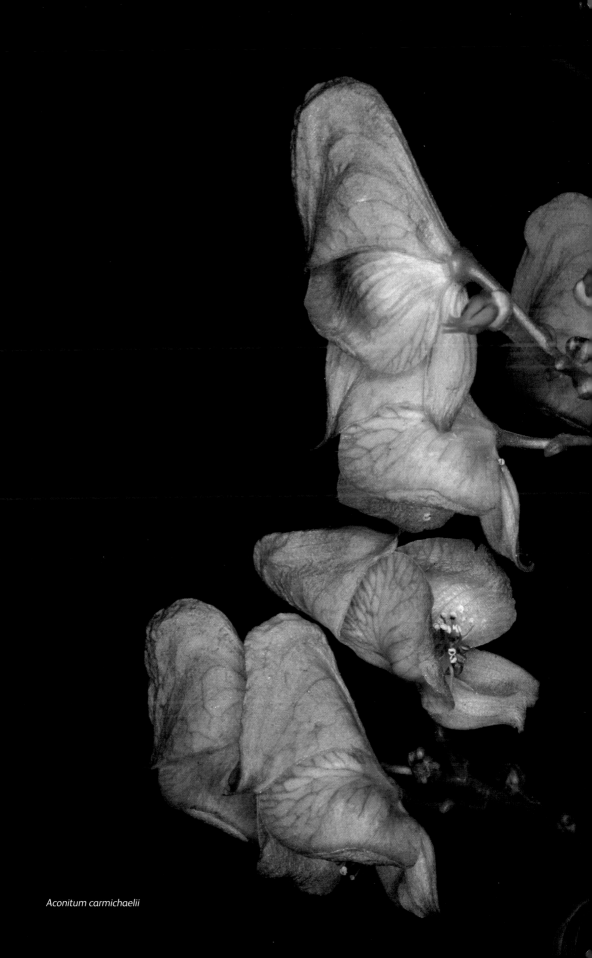

Aconitum carmichaelii

NAPELLVS.

Woodcut of *Aconitum napellus* from Mattioli (1569)

Nevertheless, physicians used the leaves for almost everything, including 'paralysis, epilepsy, rheumatic and neuralgic pains, dropsy, uterine complaints, intermittent fevers' followed by an ominous 'etc, etc.' Aconitine, present in all parts of the plant, is a highly poisonous alkaloid which causes respiratory paralysis, bradycardia (slowing of the pulse), cardiac arrhythmias, tingling, sweating, gastric cramps, diarrhoea and death, both by ingestion and by absorption through the mucous membranes and the skin. It is advisable to wear gloves when handling the plant. There is no antidote, but atropine reverses the bradycardia and may be lifesaving. The notorious 'curry murder', as it was dubbed by the London *Evening Standard* (10 February 2010), occurred in 2009 when Lakhvir Kaur Singh added *Aconitum* juice to the curry being eaten by her ex-lover and his fiancée. The man died within hours. ■

These aconitums are hardy perennials in the family Ranunculaceae. *Aconitum carmichaelii* is found in damp meadows and wooded mountains of central and west China and North America. Its tall panicles of large, hooded blue flowers appear above glossy leaves from summer to autumn. Old flowered stems can be cut down to encourage flowering, and staking may be required, otherwise it does not like to be disturbed. *Aconitum lycoctonum* subsp *neapolitanum* grows wild in damp woodlands, grassy areas and river banks throughout Eurasia. It has pretty, pale yellow flowers with long tapering hoods. At the Medicinal Garden it grows in the centre of a sunny, well-drained mixed border. Both are mulched annually with well-rotted horse manure, and can be propagated easily by sowing seed outside in a cold frame.

Aconitum napellus

Aconitum lamarckii, now Aconitum lycoctonum

Aconitum lamarckii Jean Baptiste Lamarck

I will include the Frenchman, Jean Baptiste Lamarck (1744–1829), a failed medical student, in our list of *Doctors in the Medicinal Garden*. *Aconitum lamarckii* was named after him, but the name is disappearing in favour of *Aconitum lycoctonum* subsp *neapolitanum,* which is the name we now use.

Jean Baptiste Lamarck (1744–1829)
Image: © Royal College of Physicians

He was born Jean Baptiste Pierre Antoine de Monet, Chevalier de Lamarck, in Picardy, France. As the 11th child of the impoverished lord of the manor, he started his higher education in a Jesuit College with the aim of entering the church. Three of his brothers were in the army, and he gave up his studies and joined the army at the age of 17. He survived the massacre of all but 14 of his company in the battle of Fissinghausen (1761), taking command when all the officers were killed, and on being relieved received a battlefield commission. Later, when in barracks at Toulon and Monaco, his neck was damaged during some horseplay and this forced him to resign. He studied medicine for four years but could not afford to complete his studies, so became a botanist. He published a simple dichotomous key to the French flora, *Flore francoise* (1778), in three volumes. Lamarck was appointed a royal botanist in 1779, travelling and collecting specimens and, on his return, commenced the publication of his 10-volume *Encyclopédie méthodique botanique* (1783–1823), which contained illustrations of 2,000 genera on 1,000 plates.

His enthusiasm was immense, and when the naturalist and explorer Pierre Sonnerat (1748–1814) returned from India with a large herbarium, Lamarck was the only person to visit him – an act which was rewarded by the gift of Sonnerat's herbarium. He also acquired the herbarium of Dr Philibert Commerson (1727–73), the French physician and naturalist, who accompanied Louis de Bougainville on the latter's circumnavigation of the world (1766–9). In 1788, he became keeper of the herbarium at the Royal Garden.

The French Revolution ended royal patronage and in 1793 he lost his botanical post. In the reappointment process (familiar to us today when there is a management change and all the employees have to apply for their own jobs) at the re-named Museum of Natural History in Paris, he was appointed professor of invertebrate zoology – a subject about which he knew nothing. He clearly worked hard, for his *Histoire naturelle des animaux sans vertébres* (*Natural history of invertebrates,* 7 vols, 1815–22) was highly acclaimed. However, he propounded a theory of evolution (inheritance of acquired characteristics) and many incomprehensible ideas based on spontaneous generation of animals, the interactions of the four elements of Ancient Greece (earth, air, fire and >

water) which owed everything to the traditions of alchemy and nothing to the advances in chemistry and physics, which he rejected, and published ludicrous forecasts of daily temperatures for 11 years in advance, until publicly and brutally mocked by Napoleon. His concepts of evolution have been summarised by Georges Cuvier (1836) as follows:

> It is the desire and the attempt to swim that produces membranes in the feet of aquatic birds; wading in the water, and at the same time the desire to avoid wet, has lengthened the legs of such as frequent the sides of rivers; and it is the desire of flying that has converted the arms of all birds into wings, and their hairs and scales into feathers.

He published his theories in *Recherches sur les causes des principaux faits physiques* (Research on the causes of the principal physical facts, 1794) and *Memoires de physique et d'histoire naturelle* (Memoirs on physics and natural history, 1797), which were so obviously weird that no one took any notice of them. That his theory of inheritance of acquired characteristics should still be taught and have its adherents, can only be regarded as strange, but we are fortunate that his ideas of spontaneous generation of lower plants and animals (and the geology of the planet) have (one hopes) completely disappeared. Blindness and poverty blighted his final years, but in recognition of his now forgotten monumental works of botany and invertebrate zoology, over 100 species of plants (including the small, spring-flowering tree, *Amelanchier lamarckii*, in the North American bed) and 100 marine species have been named after him (Cuvier, 1836).

Aconitum lycoctonum, Wolfsbane or Badgersbane, is probably the aconite described in Dioscorides *Materia medica* (AD 70):

Amelanchier lamarckii

> Wolfsbane, which some call lycoctonum: it grows in large quantities in Italy, on the mountain called Vestini ... They use them for hunting wolves by placing them on raw meats: for they are deadly to the wolves that eat them (Beck, 2005).

Ruellio (1543) illustrates it in his *Commentary* on Dioscorides. In around 300 BC, Theophrastus wrote extensively on its poisonous properties in his *Enquiry into plants* (Loeb edition, 1980) and in his time it was '... not lawful even to have it in one's possession, under pain of death'.

As for *A. carmichaelii*, gloves should be worn when handling all *Aconitum* species for they are all highly poisonous and even small amounts of the toxic sap are readily absorbed through the skin. ∎

Lycoctonon, Pardalianches.

Woodcut of *Aconitum lamarckii* (lyctoctonum), or *pardalianches* from Ruellio (1543)

Adonis vernalis

Adonis vernalis Adonis

Woodcut of *Adonis vernalis* from Mattioli (1569)

Adonis aestivalis, the summer *Adonis*

We grow the golden-flowered *Adonis vernalis*, the spring *Adonis*, in memory of Adonis, the Greek god of plants, who disappeared into the earth in the winter and reappeared in the spring.

The flowers were said to have sprung from his blood when he was gored to death by a wild boar, but this plant must have been the blood-red *Adonis aestivalis*, the summer *Adonis*. Not strictly medical, but as the god's charges included medicinal plants, we feel he is somewhat of an apothecary and so allowed.

Johnson (1633) reported that the ground-up seeds were good for renal stones and for intestinal colic. Although not mentioned by Dioscorides, Mattioli (1569) illustrated it as false hellebore, *pseudoelleborum*, which Pio Font Quer (1983) says contains cardiac glycosides and can be used to treat heart failure when blood levels of digoxin, and its analogues, from foxglove leaf treatment, have accumulated and are causing side effects. This seems unlikely as one would expect the cardiac glycosides in *Adonis* to have an additive rather than a counteractive effect. ∎

> *Adonis vernalis* is a hardy perennial in the Ranunculaceae family, found on sandy soils in heath, grassland and pine woodlands across Europe. It forms mounds of feathery leaves and striking buttercup-like flowers in spring. It grows happily in the Medicinal Garden at the front of a raised, well-drained border in full sun, with an annual mulch of leaf mould. On planting, the crowns should be a couple of centimetres below the soil surface. *Adonis aestivalis* is an inhabitant of farmland in southern Europe, North Africa and Asia. It is a pretty, hardy annual with feathery foliage and small, black-centred, red flowers in early summer. Seed can be sown in shallow drills, in a well-drained sunny border, then thinned out as necessary. Ripe seed can be collected and saved for sowing the following year.

Agave parryi

Agave parryi Charles Christopher Parry

Parry's *agave* is named for Charles Christopher Parry (1823–90), an English-born, American botanist and physician.

Charles Christopher Parry (1823–90). Image courtesy of the University and Jepson Herbaria Archives, University of California, Berkeley, CA USA.

Born in Gloucestershire, he moved to New York with his parents in 1832 and was a medical student at Columbia University. At college he studied botany under John Torrey, the premier botanist of the USA, and in 1848 with the physician botanist George Engelmann, the founder of the Missouri Botanical Garden. He had his practice in Davenport, Iowa, but in 1861 he spent the summer collecting the wild flowers of Colorado, acquiring 417 species. In 1862, he led a collecting party which found 700 species. For the next 20 years, he spent his summers collecting in Colorado. He travelled to England (1870), where he met Sir Joseph Hooker, the director at Kew, who was later (1878) to call Parry the 'king of Colorado botany'. He made use of both aspects of his training, as surgeon and botanist to the United States and Mexican Boundary Survey from 1848–55. He collected on the US-Mexican border in California, as well as in Colorado, Wyoming and Utah. His herbarium of 18,000 specimens is at Iowa State University, although in his lifetime he collected 30,000 specimens, 100 of which were new to science, and were an important source for Watson *et al*'s *Geological survey of California* (*Botany*, 2 volumes; 1876, 1889). He discovered the Torrey pine, *Pinus torreyana*, and the Engelmann spruce, *Picea engelmannii*, naming them after his botany teachers from Columbia. Some 80 plants are named after Parry.

Agave parryi grows in Mexico at between 1,200–2,400 metres. It is sometimes called the Mescal cactus, although this name is best reserved for other agaves. Its sap can be fermented into an alcoholic drink, mescal or mezcal, but it contains no mescaline or other hallucinogenic chemicals. Its grey-blue leaves and compact habit make it a popular garden plant in dry, semi-tropical gardens. It is monocarpic – dying after flowering. Agaves are not related to aloes, and the sap can cause severe itching due to needle-like raphides (needles) of calcium oxalate which penetrate the skin. ∎

>

Agave parryi **is a succulent in the Agavaceae family from the arid areas of southern North America. It is known as the hardiest of the species and survives happily outside at the Medicinal Garden. We grow it in a sunny position, in a sheltered, free draining border amongst other plants from arid zones. In less favourable conditions, it is advisable to grow in a pot to plunge into the border during summer and keep under glass over winter. It produces numerous offsets which can be potted up to increase stocks.**

Arisaema griffithii William Griffith

This curious plant, with frightening purple spathes, commemorates the British physician Dr William Griffith (1810–45), surgeon and botanist.

Griffith was born at Ham Common, Kingston-upon-Thames, Surrey, and qualified in medicine at London University, where he was taught botany by John Lindley. He contributed to botanical publications in Nathaniel Wallich's *Plantae Asiaticae rariores* (1832) and his extraordinary talents were recognised even then. In 1832 he started work in Madras as assistant-surgeon to the East India Company. In 1835 he accompanied Dr Wallich to botanise in the forests of Assam. Griffiths collected around 12,000 plants (and fish and birds), walking through Burma, Bhutan and Afghanistan, frequently brought down by fevers, with the object of producing a flora of India. His travels and his re-discovery of the jadeite mines in Burma (in 1837) are described in his *Journals of travels in Assam, Burma, Bootan, Afghanistan, and the neighbouring countries* (1847). In 1842–4, he became superintendent of the Calcutta Botanic Garden when Dr Wallich was away, and then took up a medical post in Malacca. He died shortly afterwards of hepatitis, aged 35, and his flora was never completed. He lived his short life to the full, enjoyed fishing, drew beautifully, and his descriptions of people record a world long vanished. He also has an orchid, *Dendrobium griffithianum*, named after him.

 Arisaema griffithii produces female flowers if well-grown, if poorly grown it has male flowers. Occasionally, a plant will produce bisexual flowers. It has an appalling smell, which attracts pollinating flies. Apparently Sherpas eat some species of *Arisaema* and use them as treatment for intestinal worms, however, their toxicity is unknown. It is possible that they are toxic when raw and made edible by cooking, in the manner of *Dioscorea* (qv) and other tubers. These arums were known as 'dragons' (*Dracunculus* in Latin) in European literature and illustrated with woodcuts. A woodcut illustration of a 'lesser dracunculus' *Dracunculus minor* used by Mathioli in 1569 was still being used by Salmon in 1710, an indication perhaps of the expense of getting new woodcuts made. ■

Arisaema griffithii of the family Araceae hails from the eastern Himalayas. In the Medicinal Garden it grows happily in a sheltered border in partial shade. In early summer, a snake-like spathe with blotched petioles dramatically appears. Well-drained, humus-rich soil is required as the corms will rot if too wet or cold. We mulch annually with well-rotted manure.

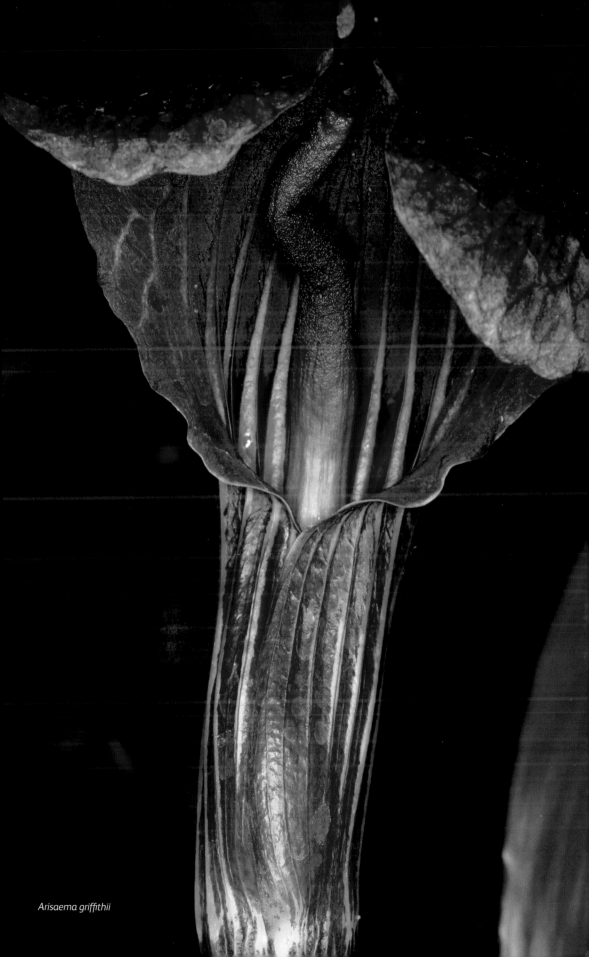

Arisaema griffithii

'His staff, with a single snake twined round it, is the symbol of medicine, and is used as the logo of the British and American Medical Associations.'

Asclepias tuberosa Asclepius (Aesculapius)

Asclepias tuberosa is named for Asclepius, the Greek god of medicine (Aesculapius in the Roman pantheon), the son of Apollo. He probably existed around 600 BC, but became a Roman god in *c*. 295 BC.

Statue of Asclepius (Aesculapius) and Telesphorus

Apollo was the god who kept disease away and Telesphorus, the short person with the woolly hat who accompanies Asclepius in the Royal College of Physicians' statue, was the god of convalescence. Asclepius was regarded as a 'hands-on' physician who intervened with drugs and surgery when a person was ill. His staff, with a single snake twined round it, is the symbol of medicine, and is used as the logo of the British Medical Association and the American Medical Association. The caduceus, two snakes twined round a winged staff, was given to Hermes, the messenger of the gods, by Apollo and is not a medical symbol, although it has been so used in error (Graf, 2009).

The mythology of Asclepius is convoluted, and there are several versions. Ovid's (AD 8) version was that his mother was Coronis, daughter of Phlegyas, king of the Lapiths. Apollo killed her when he heard she was a lover to someone else. The baby Asclepius, delivered by caesarean section from the dead Coronis as she lay on her burning funeral pyre by the repentant Apollo, was brought up by the centaur Chiron (who also brought up Achilles qv).

Asclepius became so skilled that he was able to revive the dead, and Zeus killed him with a bolt of lightning. One version states that this was at the request of Pluto, king of the Underworld, who had become worried that Asclepius might keep everyone alive so there would be no more souls to enter Hades.

Asclepias tuberosa is the American Milkweed, and is one of the host plants of the caterpillar of the Monarch butterfly, *Danaus plexippus*. The sap is highly toxic, containing >

Asclepias tuberosa

Wiſanck, ſiue Vincetoxicum Indianum.
Indian Swallow-wort.

'The plant called *asclepias* by Dioscorides is probably *Cynanchum vincetoxicum*; that of Lobel is *Cyanchum louiseae*.'

cardenolides related to digoxin. The caterpillars store it and it continues in the bodies of the butterflies, which makes them poisonous to eat. One bird, the Black-headed Grosbeak, *Pheucticus melanocephalus*, is not affected by this poison and feeds on the overwintering adults. The butterflies are capable of huge migrations, overwintering in the pine forests of Mexico and California. The plant called *asclepias* by Dioscorides is probably *Cynanchum vincetoxicum;* that of Lobel is *Cyanchum louiseae*. Our plant first appeared in Gerard (1597), 'called *Wysanck* by the savages' or *Vincetoxicum Indianum*, Virginian Silk Grasse, and the silky seeds were made into undergarments for young maidens. The woodcut in the 1597 edition, taken from the painting made by John White on one of the expeditions (1584–90) to settle Roanoke Island in what is now South Carolina, lacked the flower shown opposite in Johnson's 1633 edition of Gerard. The Latin name, *Vincetoxicum Indianum* (literally 'Indian counter-poison'), was given to it by White because 'the savages ... wherewith theie cure their wounds which they receave by the poisoned arroes of theire enemys'. One poison being an antidote to another was a familiar concept in European herbal medicine of that era. *Asclepias tuberosa* has also acquired the name 'pleurisy root' as it was used for lung infections, but because of its toxicity it is a banned substance. ∎

> **Asclepias tuberosa** is a hardy perennial in the family Apocyanaceae, bearing clusters of orange flowers on upright stems in summer. It prefers dry, fast-draining soils and grows well in the Medicinal Garden in the dappled shade of a plane tree. It has large tuberous roots, which do not like to be disturbed.

Camellia sinensis

Camellia sinensis Georg Josef Kamel

The leaves of *Camellia sinensis* are dried to make the tea we drink; the genus name commemorates Georg Josef Kamel (1661–1706), a Jesuit pharmacist born in Moravia (Czech Republic).

He went as a Jesuit priest to the Marianas in 1683 and Manila in the Philippines in 1688, and set up the first pharmacy there. He sent plants found in the gardens of the Chinese to the botanist John Ray (1627–1705) in England, who published his work in an appendix to his own *Historia plantarum* (1686–1704) as *Herbarum aliarumque stirpium in insula Luzone Philippinarum* (1704) (Herbs and other plants in the island of Luzon in the Phillipines). It is unlikely that Kamel found camellias as he never went to Japan or China, but his work on the flora of the Far East was substantial, and merited the recognition. He also wrote *Observationes de avibus Philippensibus* (1702), the first account of the birds of the Philippines.

This small shrub has not been very happy in the Medicinal Garden, probably because of the severe winter of 2010–11. The leaves are the source of tea, drunk principally for its stimulating effect. This is due mainly to its caffeine content with tiny amounts of theophylline and theobromine. The different types of tea – black, green and white – have their different flavours due solely to the preparation method and the quality of the leaf.

Tea was first brought to Europe in 1610 and by 1750 had become the British national drink, with 18,000 tonnes imported annually. It remained a monopoly for the Chinese until the beginning of the 19th century when Dr Siebold (qv under *Primula sieboldii*) smuggled seeds to Java to set up tea growing there. In 1848 and subsequent years, the British plant hunter Robert Fortune (1812–89) smuggled 100,000 tea plants and seedlings to Darjeeling, India, accompanied by Chinese tea growers, for the East India Company, and set up the Indian tea plantations. Fortune not only used the Wardian cases – water-tight boxes with glass tops – for shipping plants, but also sowed seed into earth in the cases and these germinated in transit, ready for planting out on arrival (Cox, 1945).

Frontispiece of *Herbarum aliarumque stirpium* (1704) by Georg Josef Kamel in volume 3 of *Historiae plantarum* by John Ray
Image: © Wellcome Library, London

> The evergreen *Camellia sinensis* is a frost-hardy shrub in the Theaceae family. It comes from west China, where summers are warm and wet and winters are dry and frost-free. In the Medicinal Garden it grows in a sheltered position in partial shade; dainty white, scented flowers appear in autumn and winter. It prefers rich, acidic soil, so plenty of organic matter was incorporated on planting, and during the growing season it is fed monthly with an organic, seaweed-based, fertiliser.

Dahlia merckii

Dahlia merckii Anders (Andreas) Dahl

This was named in honour of Anders (Andreas) Dahl (1751–89), the Swedish botanist and physician, by the Spanish botanist Antonio José Cavanilles (1745–1804) in 1791.

Dahl was born in Varnhem, Västergötland, Sweden, the son of the preacher Christoffer Dahl and his wife Johanna Helena Enegren. He was one of the co-founders of the 'Swedish Topographic Society in Skara' in 1769 (aged 18). Dahl studied medicine at the University of Uppsala, where he was a student of Carl Linnaeus, but did not finish his studies for financial reasons. He worked with Claes Alströmer (of *Alstroemeria*) in his botanical garden near Gothenburg, collecting plants and travelling widely. Dahl received an honorary degree in medicine from Kiel in 1786, and became associate professor and botanist at Turku University in 1787. Here he published his *Observationes botanicae circa systema vegetabilium divi a Linne* (Botanical observations on the Linnaean system of plant classification, 1787). The majority of his herbarium was destroyed by fire in 1827, but parts survive in Helsinki and Edinburgh. Dahl tried (unsuccessfully) to keep Linnaeus's herbarium in Sweden in 1783 when it was purchased by Sir James Smith for the Linnean Society of London. His friend, the botanist Carl Thunberg, named a plant *Dahlia crinita* (now *Trichocladus crinitus*) in his memory in 1792 (*crinita* is Latin for long hair in reference to Dahl's long beard). His *Horologium florae* (a floral clock) was published posthumously in 1790.

Title page of *Observationes botanicae* by Anders Dahl (1787)
Image: © Royal Botanic Gardens, Kew

This wild species of the well-known garden plant from Mexico represents a possible future for medicine. It does not suffer from mildew because it contains a gene that gives it immunity from fungal infections. This fungal-resistant gene has been experimentally inserted into the mildew-prone aubergine, to give healthy crops which do not need spraying with fungicides. Transplanting healthy genes, or epigenetic factors influencing the expression of disease genes, into people carrying genes for illnesses such as cystic fibrosis, diabetes or even schizophrenia, may be one of the possible therapies of the future. ■

> **Dahlia merckii** is a perennial in the Asteraceae family from north and central Mexico. Delicate, single lilac flowers are produced in late summer. It grows happily in partial shade near to the base of a large plane tree, but the plants are kept well watered during dry spells in the summer months. It is one of the hardiest dahlias, and the tubers survive the winter underground with a generous layer of mulch for protection.

Dieffenbachia seguine Joseph Dieffenbach

This plant is here as it was *not* named after two doctors, as alleged by countless reports on the internet and in etymological dictionaries, but after a head gardener, Joseph Dieffenbach (1790–1863).

The type plant of the genus was named *Arum seguine* in 1760 from a plant collected by the missionary Charles Plumier (1646–1704) in 1693. This was corrected when the current genus name, *Dieffenbachia*, was given by Heinrich Wilhelm Schott (1794–1865) in 1829. It could not have been named after Johan Karl Ernest Dieffenbach (1811–55), a German physician and naturalist, born in Giessen, as he was only 18 at the time. This Dr Dieffenbach had a rather stormy time as a medical student (expelled for duelling and political activity) and did not become involved in natural history until after coming to England in 1837. He has a New Zealand bird, *Gallirallus dieffenbachii*, named after him, and a Chatham Island umbelliferous plant, *Coxella dieffenbachia*, but not our genus. He translated Darwin's *Journal* into German – Darwin called him 'Devilsbach', which was not particularly kind. Equally our plant is not named after the German plastic surgeon from Berlin, Johann Friedrich Dieffenbach (1792/4–1847), who had nothing to do with botany, despite the claim for him in the book on the origin of botanical names by Helmut Genaust (1996).

> '**Equally, our plant is not named after the German plastic surgeon from Berlin, Johann Friedrich Dieffenbach (1792/4– 1847), who had nothing to do with botany.'**

Our Joseph Dieffenbach (1790–1863) was an Austrian, a long-standing head gardener at the Imperial Gardens of Schönbrunn Palace in Vienna, which belonged to the (geographically separate) Botanical Garden, now the Botanical Garden of the University of Vienna. Sources on the internet report that he brought *Dieffenbachia seguine* back from Brazil around 1830, and if true this would have been on the Austrian-Brazilian expeditions (1817–35). If he did collect it then it may well have been earlier than 1830 in order for Schott to name the genus after him in 1829, using *D. seguine* as the type specimen (note: this is the plant which was used as the first example of the genus). Schott had been a botanist on at least the first expedition (1817–21), before becoming director of the Schönbrunn Palace Gardens from 1845–65. Stephan Ladislaus Endlicher was director of the Botanic Gardens from 1839–49, and Dieffenbach worked with him from 1841 to redesign the open areas of that garden in the English landscaping style and, from 1849, under Eduard Fenzl, Endlicher's successor. Additionally, Schott's father had been a gardener at Schönbrunn, >

Dieffenbachia seguine

where Joseph Dieffenbach worked, so the evidence for our Joseph Dieffenbach being a person well known to Schott and so honoured by the name of the plant genus is overwhelming (Stearn, 1996).

This is 'Dumb Cane', so called as the West Indian species, *Dieffenbachia seguine*, was said to have been given as punishment to slaves, causing a very painful swollen mouth and excessive saliva. The leaves have cells (idioblasts) containing needle-like crystals of calcium oxalate (raphides), and when chewed these are injected into the soft tissues of the mouth, tongue and pharynx, causing irritation and such swelling of the lips and tongue as to render one incapable of speech. The same chemicals are found in taro, the root of *Colocasia esculenta* (pictured opposite), a staple food in Africa and Asia. Prolonged soaking or boiling the tubers renders them edible. There was a huge evolutionary advantage in being able to eat tubers which were inedible – and poisonous – when raw. The poisonous alkaloid content of yams (*Dioscorea*), of cyanogenic glycosides (cyanide) in cassava (*Manihot esculenta*), and the calcium oxalate in taro can be removed by boiling, so when humans discovered cooking they had access to an abundant food source for which they did not have to compete with other animals. ■

Dieffenbachia seguine, in the family Araceae, is a tender perennial distributed from Mexico to South America. In the UK, it is usually kept as a houseplant, but in the Medicinal Garden we grow it in shaded pots outside in summer and in a heated glasshouse in winter. The potting mix is equal parts loam, sand and bark. As the plant matures the lower leaves die and are not replaced, so creating the cane. If the plant becomes too tall it is possible to prune back into the cane in early spring, causing the plant to sprout from lower leaf nodes. They are kept well watered during summer, allowing them to become almost dry between soakings. They are fed fortnightly with a balanced liquid fertiliser.

Colocasia esculenta

Dioscorea batatas

Dioscorea batatas Pedanius Dioscorides

Dioscorea, the yam, is also named after Pedanius Dioscorides (qv under *Acanthus dioscoridis*). The genus includes some 600 plants, and those with tubers are a hugely important food crop across the world – the third largest source of carbohydrate.

The raw tubers are poisonous, different species containing varying amounts of toxic steroidal saponins, diterpenoids and/or alkaloids, which are removed by prolonged boiling or soaking in salt water, so they are not eaten by other animals. The literature on what makes yams poisonous is vague and often contradictory. Nevertheless, mankind's ability to cook them, and the plant's ability to be stored without refrigeration for up to six months in the tropics, makes its cultivation one of the most important factors in the evolution of civilisations. A surplus of food allowed sections of the population to develop other occupations besides food gathering, so large urban communities became viable. Asian species are less toxic than African ones, but selective breeding is reducing the alkaloid content of the tubers, which will reduce the amount of wood needed to be cut down to do the cooking, but will make the tuber edible to other hungry animals. Harvesting is interesting as there are yams with elongated tubers two metres in length (they grow vertically like carrots), so much digging is required. The sweet potato (*Ipomoea batatas*) is sometimes called a yam, but is no relation of *Dioscorea*. Death from eating inadequately prepared yams occurs, and they have been used to murder, to commit suicide, as an arrow poison and a fishing bait poison in Africa, South America and especially in south-east Asia. Additionally, it is used in various herbal medicine preparations, and is found to induce hypoglycaemia.

In 1943, Professor Russell Marker discovered a method of obtaining an unsaturated steroidal saponine, diosogenin, from Mexican yam (*Dioscorea mexicana*), which can easily and cheaply be converted into steroids, such as prednisone and progesterone, reducing the price of steroid production to a fraction (0.5%) of its former cost. For 20 years drug companies showed little interest, and it was only as a result of Professor Marker forming his own company, and the concerted efforts of several gynaecologists, physiologists and birth-control advocates, that the contraceptive pill was 'born' in 1960. Professor Marker's discovery led the way to synthetic anabolic steroids, as used by Ben Johnson in the 1988 Olympics to run faster than he should have done, as well as to treatments for almost everything from arthritis to eczema. There is a nice sense of serendipity that a plant which was responsible for part of the global population explosion is now being taken by 100 million women worldwide to try to curb it. ■

Dodecatheon meadia

Dodecatheon meadia (now *Primula meadia*), a hardy perennial in the family Primulaceae, is found in the woods and prairies of eastern USA, and requires similar growing conditions to *Primula veris*. It forms graceful white or pink reflexed flowers in spring and early summer. It becomes dormant when conditions become dry in late summer.

Dodecatheon meadia Richard Mead

This spring-flowering 'Shooting star' from North America, is named for Dr Richard Mead FRCP FRCPE FRS (1673–1754), physician to St Thomas' Hospital and later to King George II.

Mead came from Stepney, London, and, after initial schooling at home, studied at Utrecht (1688) and then Leiden (1692), from whence he qualified in physic in 1695. In the same year, he gained a medical degree at Padua. He practised medicine in Stepney until 1702, when he published *A mechanical account of poisons*. He was elected FRS and became physician to St Thomas' Hospital in 1703, and the reader in anatomy to the barber surgeons. In 1707 he was elected vice-president of the Royal Society, and Oxford University awarded him the degree of doctor of medicine. He took over the private practice of Dr Radcliffe and resigned from St Thomas' in 1714. Following this he took and passed the (Royal) College of Physicians exam, becoming a fellow in 1716. He held numerous posts, but declined the office of president in 1744. In 1745, he was elected an honorary fellow of the Royal College of Physicians of Edinburgh. Mead became immensely rich, with a practice income of over £6,000 a year, acquired a huge library and art collection, was a generous host and lived a lavish life style which probably bankrupted him in the end (Munk, 1878).

Dr Richard Mead FRCP FRCPE FRS (1673–1754)
Image: © Royal College of Physicians

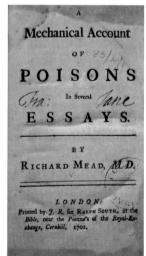

Frontispiece of *A mechanical account of poisons* (1702) by Dr Richard Mead FRCP FRCPE FRS. Image: © Royal College of Physicians

Dodecatheon meadia has no medicinal value but was, apparently, eaten in emergencies by Native Americans. It is in the primrose family, which are not known for much use except as ornamental plants. *Dodecatheon meadia* was first described and illustrated as *Meadia* in the appendix to Mark Cotesby's *Natural history of Carolina ...* (1747) as: 'To this new genus of Plants I have given the name of the learned Dr Richard Mead, Physician to His Majesty, and F.R.S., in gratitude for his gracious patronage of the Arts and Sciences in general, and in particular for his generous assistance towards carrying the original design of this work into execution'. ■

Dodonaea viscosa Rembert Dodoens

ROMBERTVS DODONAEVS
MECHLINIENSIS.

Moribus & fide te testor Romberte valere,
Usui nempe tuis saepue hospitys.
Quod Medicus valeas Mechlinia dicet & horti
Quos steruit, in plantis quantus es, atque libris.

This small shrub from New Zealand gets its name from the Flemish physician Rembert Dodoens (1517–85). He studied geography, medicine and cosmology at Leuven (Louvain), Belgium, graduating in 1538.

Dodoens practised initially in Mechelen (Malines) in the province of Antwerp. Later, while working in Basel (1542–6), he prepared the material for his important herbal, the *Cruydeboeck* (published in 1554). He was still physician in Mechelen in 1558, becoming physician to the Austrian emperor Rudolph II from 1575–8, and thereafter was professor of medicine at Leiden from 1582 until his death.

The *Cruydeboeck* had over 700 woodcuts of plants, mostly copies of those in Leonhart Fuchs' herbal, *De historia stirpium commentarii insignes* (Notable commentaries on the history of plants, the small octavo, 1551 edition, not the large quarto first edition of 1542) and the text follows the same format. Dodoens translated his *Cruydeboeck* into Latin with the title *Stirpium historiae pemptades sex* (1583), which was in turn translated into English by Dr Priest of the College of Physicians (later to be known as the Royal College of Physicians), and published by John Gerard as his *Herball, or General historie of plantes* (1597). Quite why Gerard bothered is obscure as it had already been translated into English and published as *A nievve Herball or historie of Plantes* (1578) by Henry Lyte. Lyte's version was translated from the French translation of the *Cruydeboeck*, the *Histoire des plantes* (1588), made by Charles de L'Escluse (also known as l'Écluse and/or Carolus Clusius), and while it is in the same >

A 16th century drawing of Rembert Dodoens after the engraving in *A nievve Herball or historie of Plantes*, translated by Henry Lyte (1578)

> '*Dodonaea viscosa* has few traditional and no current medicinal uses, but in Hawaii the crushed leaves are used to treat skin rashes.'

Dodonaea viscosa

Dodonaea viscosa

'The winged fruits are bitter to taste, and it gained its common name of Australian Hop Bush because Australian brewers, lacking hops, added the fruits to beer to impart a bitter taste.'

order as the original it has large sections (eg *Equisetum*) omitted. Gerard's version seems more complete, but the order is completely different from Lyte's. All these books were enormously influential in plant-based medicine by virtue of their extensive illustrations, but their debt to Fuchs is obvious.

Dodonaea viscosa has few traditional and no current medicinal uses, but in Hawaii the crushed leaves are used to treat skin rashes. It contains numerous chemicals – as do all plants – most importantly poisonous cyanogenic glycosides which are toxic to cattle and cause liver damage. *Dr Duke's phytochemical and ethnobotanical databases*, on the internet, lists just over 50 chemicals to be found in it, for which he claims 313 potential medicinal uses. It is unlikely that any of these chemicals will ever be used. It has spread across the world, becoming an invasive weed in south western USA, and in the Peruvian Andes north of Huanuco, where it covers hectares of steep slopes with its scrubby vegetation.

The winged fruits are bitter to taste, and it gained its common name of Australian Hop Bush because Australian brewers, lacking hops, added the fruits to beer to impart a bitter taste. The aborigines chew the leaves (without swallowing the juice) to relieve toothache and use it as a poultice to relieve the pain of stonefish and stingray injuries. In Peru, the leaves are reportedly (Williams, 2010) chewed as a stimulant and used to adulterate coca leaves (*Erythroxylum coca*), to which they bear no obvious resemblance except being flat. ∎

This vigorous, frost-hardy, evergreen shrub, in the family Sapindaceae comes from open woodland on well-drained soils in South Africa, Australia and Mexico. This cultivar has handsome red-purple foliage which, at the back of the border, acts as an attractive backdrop for other plants from the southern hemisphere. Its leaves are protected by a sticky exudate, which helps it to resist drought and pollution from London traffic. Cutting back into old wood is not advisable, but it responds well to light clipping in spring to maintain a balanced shape. All our specimens were killed in the –10°C frosts of 2010–11 and have been replaced.

Opposite page: Woodcut of Rembert Dodoens, aged 35, from Henry Lyte's *A nievve Herball or historie of Plantes* (1578)

Doctors in the Medicinal Garden

REMBERTI
DODONÆI
ÆTA. XXXV.

VIRTVTE
AMBI.

Ephedra gerardiana var *sikkimensis*
James Gilbert Gerard

A primitive plant from which ephedrine was extracted and amphetamines (and thereafter Ecstasy) were synthesised.

It looks like a Mare's Tail (*Equisetum*) and is named for James Gilbert Gerard (1793–1835), a Scottish army surgeon in the Bengal Medical Service who collected plants in the Himalayas (and not for John Gerard the 16th/17th century surgeon/herbalist). He served in Nepal in 1815 with the Gurkhas in the 1st Nasiri Battalion of the British army in Bengal, and his grave at Subathu notes his death on 31 March 1835 at the age of 42. While in Sabathu he was paid 80 rupees a month for superintending the Vaccine Establishment there (1823–4), but later records show that he travelled on full military pay through Afghanistan and Central Asia (1831–3).

The plant is also named for his two brothers, Patrick (1794–1848), a meteorologist, and Alexander (1792–1839), a scientist. On his younger brother's grave (Captain Patrick Gerard, of the same regiment) in Simla, it notes how the three brothers were among the first to explore the Trans-Himalayan regions. Captain Alexander Gerard was in the 27th Native Infantry and his two-volume *Narrative of a journey from Caunpoor to the Boorendo pass in the Himalaya Mountains viâ Gwalior, Agra, Delhi, and Sirhind* (1810, with others), and *A map of Koonawar* and *Account of Koonawar in the Himalaya* (published posthumously, 1841) from his travels in 1817 and 1818 (accompanied on this occasion by James) have little of botanical interest. Alexander died of malaria, which recurred while back in Aberdeen. They were responsible for the discovery of Simla, then in deep forest but later an important European residential area. They do seem to have spent years doing nothing else than walking (and no 'soldiering') where few, if any, Europeans had ever been before, surveying and recording.

Berries of Ephedra gerardiana var sikkimensis

There are around 50 species of *Ephedra* found from Asia to the Mediterranean, and in North and South America. It is a primitive plant, but has flowers and berries unlike the very similar Mare's Tail, *Equisetum*, which has neither. The American species do not contain ephedrine, but this powerful alkaloid, whose sympathomimetic action is similar to adrenaline and noradrenaline, was isolated from one of the Asian species in 1897 by Nagai, from Japan. Its properties were >

Ephedra gerardiana var sikkimensis

discovered by an American, Carl Schmidt, working in Beijing with KK Chen. It was found to be useful in asthma, but stimulating effects on the heart and nervous system made it unsatisfactory, and now it is mainly to be found in nasal decongestants. It was noted by Pliny the Elder (AD 79) to stop bleeding; now known to be because of its vasoconstrictor action. It was used by the Chinese, who call it 'ma huang', for stopping coughs. Abuse by athletes led to several deaths. Methamphetamine was synthesised from it in 1929 and became a much-abused drug for its effect on preventing sleep; psychosis was occasionally reported. Ecstasy, methylenedioxymethamphetamine (MDMA), is a further derivative with other 'designer drugs'. ■

> Found on rocky inclines ranging from Afghanistan to China and the Indian subcontinent, this creeping shrub with scale-like leaves is a hardy member of the family Ephedraceae. In the Medicinal Garden it provides an excellent evergreen ground cover for dry soil at the base of a large plane tree. The variety *sikkimensis* is more vigorous than the type species which also grows happily nearby. It is easily propagated by careful division of plants in spring.

Eupatorium rugosum (now Ageratina altissima) 'Chocolate'

Eupatorium rugosum (now Ageratina altissima) 'Chocolate' Mithridates VI Eupator

This is the White Snake Root of North American woods, which gained its Latin name from Mithridates VI Eupator (134–63 BC), after whom a complex, and mythological, potion – a Mithridate – to cure all poisoning is named.

He was King of Pontus and Armenia Minor (now northern Turkey), engaged in huge wars against Rome and indulged in brutal genocides. He is more famous for his interest in antidotes to poisons. Leonhart Fuchs writes (excerpted from the 1999 facsimile and commentary on his herbal of 1542):

> *Mithridates, indeed, mighty king of Pontus and the Parthians, was not content to have won renown for his skill in 22 languages and from his various victories; but that he might become more famous and illustrious, he applied himself energetically to the business of obtaining exact knowledge of all medicinal simples, especially those that were antidotes to deadly poisons.*

His father, Mithridates V, was assassinated by poison in 120 BC, so Eupator reportedly developed immunity to poisons by regularly consuming sub-lethal doses. When he was finally defeated and in exile in the Crimea he tried to commit suicide by poison, but it had no effect, so he had to ask a loyal army officer to kill him with his sword to avoid capture by the Romans.

Eupatorium rugosum contains a chemical, tremetol, which is poisonous to cattle, killing them in days. Milk, cheese and meat from poisoned cattle also contain tremetol and caused >

'His father, Mithridates V, was assassinated by poison in 120 BC, so Eupator reportedly developed immunity to poisons by regularly consuming sub-lethal doses.'

Agrimonia eupatoria gains its species name from Mithridates VI Eupator, king of Pontus

Eupatorium rugosum (now Ageratina altissima) 'Chocolate'

the death of the mother of Abraham Lincoln (Stewart, 2009). 'Eupatoria' was the name used by Pliny for *Agrimonia eupatoria*.

We also grow *Eupatorium purpureum* subsp *maculatum*, 'Purple Boneset'. Austin (2004) reports many Native American uses: the roots were used as a laxative (Mahuna); as a breath freshner (Meskwaki); for postpartum bleeding (Menomini and Potawatomi); as a poultice for burns (Potawatomi) and as inhaled vapour from infusions for colds (Ojibwa). Milspaugh (1974) writes that it was used as a diuretic and stimulant, as an astringent tonic, for dropsy (heart failure), strangury, small urinary stones, haematuria, gout and rheumatism. Toxic effects noted are salivation, stomach cramps, urgency of micturition, tachycardia, faintness and sleepiness. ∎

> 'It is very attractive to butterflies and bees and grows in any fertile, moist soil in sun or partial shade.'

This hardy perennial known as White Snake Root originates from lowland woods in North America. It bears pure white flowers from September to November, and is disease-resistant. At the Medicinal Garden we grow the cultivar 'Chocolate' which has purple foliage. It is very attractive to butterflies and bees, and grows in any fertile, moist soil in sun or partial shade. It is mulched each spring with well-rotted manure and cut back after flowering. It can be propagated by division.

EVPATORIVM VVLGARE.

Euphorbia milii Euphorbus

'Crown of thorns' is an exotic scarlet-flowered spurge, from the genus named for Euphorbus (fl. circa 10 BC – AD 20), the Greek physician to the Berber king Juba II (*c.* 50 BC – AD 23) of Numidia, a country which once existed within modern Tunisia and Algeria.

TITHYMALVS CHARACIAS.

Euphorbia characias from Mattioli (1569)

He was the brother of Antonio Musa (*vide Musa*), physician to Caesar Augustus. The king married Cleopatra Selene, the daughter of Mark Anthony and Cleopatra, and later, Glaphyra, the widow of the son of Herod the Great. The king was interested in plants and, according to Pliny the Elder (Pliny, AD 79), gave it its name in 12 BC. In the 16th century it was known as *Tithymalus*, but Linnaeus restored the name *Euphorbia* in 1753. One story is that Euphorbus cured King Juba from a stomach condition with a *Euphorbia*. The other is that the plant was discovered by the king in the Atlas mountains of Morocco and that, as Euphorbus was a fat man and the plant was fleshy, he thought it an apt name as 'euphorbus' in Greek means 'eu = good' and 'phorbe = fodder'. Juba is remembered elsewhere, for he gives his name to the capital of the new country of South Sudan. *Euphorbia regis-jubae*, discovered on an expedition to the Canary Islands, sponsored by King Juba, also commemorates him.

   Euphorbia milii is one of the tropical spurges, with fierce, cactus-like spines, grown as a houseplant. The sap of spurges is used in folk medicine for treating warts (not very effective) and, historically, as a purgative – the word 'spurge' being derived from the French word for purgation. The sap (probably dried) was administered inside a fig because it is so corrosive that it would otherwise burn the mouth and oesophagus – a technique used today, rather more subtly, with 'enteric-coated' medications. The sap contains a potential >

'**Euphorbus was a fat man and as the plant was fleshy, he thought it an apt name as "euphorbus" in Greek means "*eu* = good" and "*phorbe* = fodder".**'

Euphorbia milii

Euphorbia
amygdaloides.

June 17.15 Publish'd by J. Sowerby London

Euphorbia amygdaloides from Sowerby (1832–46)

Euphorbia amygdaloides subsp robbiae

Euphorbia myrsinites

anti-leukaemic chemical, lasiodiplodin, and is also used in drainage ditches to kill the snails which carry the parasitic trematode which causes fasciolaris (Leet *et al*, 1982; Vasconcellos *et al*, 2003).

We grow eight other spurges as well as the well-known self-seeding weed 'petty spurge', *Euphorbia peplus. Euphorbia pulcherrima,* the scarlet-bracted poinsettia, is sold by the millions every Christmas and is of great economic importance. Even more important is the rubber tree, *Hevea brasiliensis,* in the family Euphorbiaceae, from which we obtain natural rubber. The third largest source of carbohydrate for food is another member of this family, cassava or manioc, *Manihot esculenta,* which contains high concentrations of cyanogenic glycosides and needs lengthy boiling to render it safe. The sap of all of them can cause intense skin reactions, and the smoke from burning them is toxic. We grow several of the temperate spurges, *Euphorbia amygdaloides* subsp *robbiae, E. characias* subsp *wulfenii, E. lathyris, E.* x *martini, E. nicaeensis, E. pithyusa.* ■

From Madagascar, this spiny, succulent shrub in the family Euphorbiaceae bears bright, red flowers. At the College it grows in a pot on a sheltered, sunny terrace and is overwintered in a heated glasshouse. It is re-potted carefully each year.

Fargesia rufa

Fargesia rufa Paul Guillaume Farges

We also grow *Fargesia nitida, F. scabrida, F. jiuzhaigou* and *F. robusta*, bamboos named after Paul Guillaume Farges (1844–1912), a French missionary and plant collector.

Little is known about him, but as he worked in a hospital (albeit as the almoner) at the end of his life, he has been included. He came to China in 1867 with the Missions Étrangères, stationed in the mountainous area of T'chen-keou-tin in the sub-prefecture of Ch'eng k'ou t'ing (Cheng-kou) in north-east Szechuan and worked in a practical manner, organising relief for the miserably poor inhabitants of the area. In 1892, around Cheng-kou, until 1903 he botanised extensively, sending herbarium specimens back to the botanist Adrien René Franchet (1834–1900) at the Museum of Natural History in Paris. By 1896 he had sent back 2,000 specimens, many from the mountains at 1,200–2,500 metres and above. By the time he left Cheng-kou, he had collected 4,000 herbarium specimens.

He sent seeds back to the nursery of de Vilmorin in France, including 37 seeds of the handkerchief tree, *Davidia involucrata* – possibly bringing these back himself. *Davidia involucrata* seeds take 18 months to germinate, and they were thought to be dead until one germinated in 1899, coming into flower in 1906. The nursery of James Veitch in England was so excited by this tree that they sent EH Wilson (1876–1930) to collect more seed. Wilson's success, and Messrs Veitch's happiness, can be measured in that 13,000 plants were raised from the seed he sent back, but the distinction of having introduced the tree to Europe remains with Farges. The area where he worked, especially Ta-pa-shan, was very rich in trees and shrubs and some of the best rhododendrons in cultivation in Europe, *Rhododendron discolor, R. fargesii* and *R. sutchuense*, were found by him. He moved to Choqqing in 1903, became almoner to the hospital and gave up collecting. He died there in 1912. Some 80 plants have been named after him, including the willow, *Salix fargesii*, which we also grow in the Medicinal Garden in the expectation that, like European willows, its bark contains salicylates, the basis for aspirin (Cox, 1945; Bretschneider, 1898).

Fargesia bamboo species have no medicinal uses, and are mainly grown as ornamentals, for basket work, plant supports and hedging. *Fargesia rufa* was introduced to English gardens about 15 years ago, with thin, blue-green 2.5 metre high stems decorated with pink to orange sheaths in the summer. It is reliably hardy and forms dense thickets up to 1.4 metres wide. ∎

> In the family Poaceae, *Fargesia rufa* is native to upland areas of China. It has unusual blue-green foliage and arching, green canes with pink to orange sheaths. It is a very hardy, clump-forming bamboo which likes a damp, humus-rich soil in partial shade. It is mulched annually with well-rotted horse manure. The canes can be thinned out when dormant in the winter. It is best propagated by division, when the plants begin to grow in spring.

Fothergilla gardenii John Fothergill

Dr John Fothergill LRCP FRCPE FRS (1712–80)
Image: © Royal College of Physicians

This small shrub with fragrant, white bottle-brush flowers, was named by Linnaeus for Dr John Fothergill LRCP FRCPE FRS (1712–80), the greatest plant and shell collector of the age, and Dr Alexander Garden (see *Gardenia*).

Fothergill was born in Yorkshire and commenced as an apprentice apothecary in 1728, but proceeded to Edinburgh University, where he qualified as a doctor in 1736 with a doctoral thesis on *De emeticorum usu in variis morbis tractandis* (Of the use of emetics in various illnesses, 1736). He then took what would now be called a 'gap year' (but of four years) travelling around Europe, before starting medical practice in London in 1740.

Fothergill became a licentiate of the Royal College of Physicians in 1744, and his Quaker friends helped him in his practice. He lectured on mouth-to-mouth resuscitation at the Royal Society (1745); published as *Observations on a case ... of recovering a man dead in appearance by distending the lungs with air*; published the first account of diphtheria, *An account of the sore throat attended with ulcers* (1748 – the 5th and subsequent editions were entitled *An account of the putrid sore throat*); and described trigeminal neuralgia, *Of a painful affection of the face* (1776).

He became extremely successful with an income of over £7,000 a year and purchased a large estate at Upton, now West Ham Park, with a five-acre walled garden. Fothergill spared no expense to obtain and cultivate exotic plants from all over the world for his garden, which was visited by international dignitaries and botanists. His greenhouse extended for 80 metres and contained over 3,000 species. He had the flowers painted and on his death the collection of around 2,000 paintings was sold, ending up with the Empress of Russia. He was elected to the FRCPE in 1754 and FRS in June 1763, with >

A member of the family Hamamelidaceae, this deciduous, hardy shrub from the coastal plains of south-east USA forms a small, spreading clump in a raised bed in dappled shade in the Medicinal Garden. Bottle-brush shaped spikes of white flowers appear in spring and the leaves blush red and orange in autumn. They prefer slightly acidic, damp soil, which is rich in organic matter. We mulch with well-rotted compost and leaf mould annually and prune out dead and damaged wood after flowering. Cold, drying winds can be damaging, so if possible a sheltered site should be chosen.

Fothergilla gardenii

'Fothergill spared no expense to obtain and cultivate exotic plants from all over the world.'

numerous honours from overseas. He campaigned against slavery, tried to act as an intermediary to prevent the American War of Independence, set up schools for the poor, and worked with the prison reformer, John Howard. He died from 'suppression of urine', presumably from a urinary calculus (Munk, 1878; Elliott, 1781). A charming description of him has come down to us (Elliott, 1781):

> *The person of Dr Fothergill* (says Dr Hird) *was of a delicate, rather of an extenuated make. His features were all character. His eye had a peculiar brilliance of expression; ... He was remarkably active and alert, and, with a few exceptions, enjoyed a general good state of health. His dress was remarkably neat, plain, and decent ... a perfect transcript of the order, and, I may add, of the neatness of his mind. He thought it unworthy a man of sense, and inconsistent with his character, to suffer himself to be led by the whims of fashion, and become the slave of caprice.* ∎

Fuchsia magellanica Leonhart Fuchs

Inuida multorum te exercuit vſque Voluntas,
Vera tuis creuit ſed Medicina ſcholis.
Herbas in primis noras, καὶ φάρμακα ταῦτα,
Contrahere artifici ſenſûque lata modo.

Fuschia triphylla was discovered by Charles Plumier (1646–1704) in Hispaniola in 1696/7, and the genus named by him for Leonhart Fuchs (1501–66) in 1703.

Fuchs was born in Bavaria and obtained his MA in Greek, Latin, Hebrew and philosophy in 1521 and his MD at the University of Ingolstadt in 1524. He practised in Munich, became professor of medicine at Ingolstadt in 1526, and went to the University of Tübingen in 1533, setting up its botanical garden in 1535. This was still the era before 'botany'; the study of plants being considered a branch of medicine and pharmacy.

He followed the writings of Dioscorides, Hippocrates and Galen; Fuch's magnificent herbal, *De historia stirpium commentarii insignes* (Notable commentaries on the history of plants, 1542), attempted the identification of the plants used by these earlier writers. It also contained the first accounts of maize, *Zea mays*, and chilli peppers, *Capsicum annuum*, recently introduced from Latin America. Surprisingly he was also the first person to publish an account and woodcuts of foxgloves, *Digitalis purpurea* and *D. lutea*. The book contains 500 descriptions and woodcuts of medicinal plants, arranged in alphabetical order, and relied heavily on the *De materia medica* (c. AD 70) of Dioscorides. He was a powerful influence on the herbals of Dodoens, and thence to Gerard, L'Escluse and Henry Lyte. A small quarto edition appeared in 1551, and a two-volume facsimile of the 1542 edition with commentary and selected translations from the Latin was published by Stanford Press in 1999. The original woodcuts were passed from printer to printer and continued in use for 232 years (Schinz, 1774). >

Digitalis.

'This was still the era before 'botany'; the study of plants being considered a branch of medicine and pharmacy.'

Fuchsia magellanica

Fuchsia magellanica painted by Lady Atholl Oakeley in circa 1828

'In Chile *Fuchsia magellanica* is known as Chilco, the name used by the original indigenous peoples, the Mapuche.'

Fuchsias are predominantly found in Central and South America, with three from New Zealand and one from Tahiti. In all, there are around 100 species. In Chile *F. magellanica* is known as Chilco, the name used by the original indigenous peoples, the Mapuche. They are popular garden and greenhouse plants and thousands of hybrids have been made and are now grown. In 1828, my great-great-grandmother painted *F. magellanica* at the vicarage at Bocking. ■

Fuchsia magellanica, an upright shrub in the family Onagraceae, originates in mountainous regions of Chile and Argentina. In the Medicinal Garden it grows in partial shade at the back of a border of southern hemisphere plants, where it produces pendulous, crimson flowers continuously from July to October. It is reliably hardy, surviving winters to –10°C in the Medicinal Garden with a dry mulch of bark chips for protection. Side branches may be pruned back as it is coming into leaf to shape the plant and cuttings can be taken from new growth in spring.

Gardenia jasminoides

Gardenia jasminoides Alexander Garden

This, the Cape Jasmine, was named for Dr Alexander Garden FRS (1730–91), Scottish-born physician and naturalist who lived in Charles Town (now Charleston), South Carolina, and corresponded with Linnaeus and many of the botanists of his era.

Widely honoured in his day as a botanist and 'the most famous physician of colonial times' (McCrady, 1897), he might have disappeared forever into the mists of history, save for the plants named after him.

His father was the minister of the church in Birse, in north-east Scotland, and here Garden acquired his love of nature and books. He entered Marischal College (University of Aberdeen) in 1743 (aged 13) as apprentice to Dr James Gordon, the professor of medicine. In 1746 he went to London, and after an interview with the navy, passed the exam at Surgeon's Hall, qualifying as a surgeon's second mate. He failed to get a posting so returned to Aberdeen to continue working with Professor Gordon until 1748. He then retook the examination, this time passing as eligible to be a surgeon's first mate on any ship. He first worked on a small vessel, HMS *Tryton*, and then in 1749 on HMS *Eagle*, but transferred to a small sloop called the *Porcupine*, which he disliked. He returned to his studies in Edinburgh, qualifying in 1751. He did not have the money to pay for his degree certificate, which he needed to practise in Scotland, and was suffering from tuberculosis, so decided to emigrate to a warmer climate.

On the invitation of Dr William Rose he sailed to South Carolina in 1752 and set up practice with him. Within 10 days of arrival he had become fascinated by the new plants he encountered, sending a parcel of 'pink root' (*Spigelia merilandica*, a once-popular, highly-toxic remedy for intestinal worms) back to Dr Rutherford in Edinburgh. He became interested in plant poisons with which the slaves were allegedly poisoning their owners – he did not believe this – and noted their knowledge of these matters. His illness confined him to bed for nine weeks, but he started a correspondence with the Rev Stephen Hales (qv under *Halesia*) in England which continued until his death. He collected seeds, sending them back to England, received his degree from Marischal College in 1755 and, having seen a copy of Linnaeus's *Critica botanica* in 1755, commenced to correspond with him (Linnaeus did not reply until 1759) and many other botanists in Europe. In 1755, he accompanied the governor of Charles Town into Cherokee country, which he found botanically very interesting.

He married Elizabeth Peronneau on Christmas day 1759. They were to have three surviving children, coming through the smallpox epidemic of 1761 – Garden inoculated many of the residents. During the next decades he sent plants and animals, some new to science, back to the English botanist John Ellis in London and to Linnaeus in Sweden. He sent back the first electric eel, discovered the Congo snake, *Amphiuma means*, >

and the mud eel, *Siren lacertina*. Ellis named the Cape Jasmine, *Gardenia jasminoides*, – which arrived in England from Asia in 1750, but was believed to have been a South African plant – after him in 1761. Many of the indigenous plants that he sent back to Europe were grown in his elaborate garden in Otranto, outside Charleston (Cothran, 1995). He was elected FRS in 1773. Such was the wealth of his correspondence that his name is the most frequently quoted in the last edition of Linnaeus' *Systema naturae* (1793). Linnaeus, aware of his long correspondence with Dr John Fothergill (who had sponsored the botanical travels of the American botanist John Bartram in Carolina) joined their names in naming *Fothergilla gardenii* (qv).

He supported the British side during the American War of Independence and was consequently exiled and had to return to London (1783), losing all his fortune and property as a result. His hopes of continuing his study of Californian botany in retirement were abruptly ended. However, his son (also Alexander) fought on the side of the revolutionary army in 1780 and his father's estates were restored to him. He became active within the Royal Society in London, becoming its vice-president. However, his health remained poor and he died of tuberculosis in 1791 (Berkeley, 1969).

The fragrant flowers are used in the *lei* necklaces of the Hawaiian islands, and as a buttonhole for formal celebrations, like weddings, in Britain. In warmer, temperate climates the plants are used in gardens and as hedging. The fruits are used in China both as a source of a yellow dye and for various unsubstantiated medicinal uses. Other species of *Gardenia* are found in tropical Africa, and the roots and leaves have all manner of putative uses. *Gardenia tenuifolia* is used as an aphrodisiac, for rickets, diarrhoea, leprosy, gall bladder problems, toothache, liver complaints, diabetes, hypertension, malaria and abdominal complaints. It causes violent vomiting and diarrhoea, which reflects the toxic nature of most plants, and it and other species are used to poison arrows and to poison fish. Some native healers regard *Gardenia* as a 'last chance' medicine, given to patients when all else fails – the patient either dies or recovers (Neuwinger, 1996). While many sources play down the toxicity to humans, concentrating on the toxicity to dogs and cats, they are best avoided as an article of diet or medicine. ■

Fothergilla gardenii

Gaultheria procumbens Jean-François Gaultier

This heather-like North American plant with bell-shaped flowers and scarlet berries has local names such as Eastern Teaberry, Checkerberry and Boxberry. It was named for the French physician and botanist, Jean-François Gaultier (1708–56).

He was born in France, practised medicine in Paris and became physician to the king in 1741. He was friendly with the botanists from the Académie Royale des Sciences in Paris, Antoine de Jussieu (1686–1758) and Bernard de Jussieu (1699–1777), and it may well be that his interest in botany was already evident then. He sailed to Canada in 1742 where he became involved in plant collecting and the fur trade, practising medicine in Quebec at the Hôtel-Dieu Hospital. He set up the first meteorological station in Canada (1742), but his major botanical work was a 400-page manuscript on the plants of Canada in preparation for a six-volume book on the flora of North America. This was never published because of the war between the French Canadians and the English. He helped the botanist Pehr Kalm to explore the area around Quebec (1749), and the grateful Kalm named *Gaultheria* in his honour. By 1752, his income from his salary and the fur trade was considerable and he married a rich widow who (or which) made him very happy. General Montcalm's arrival in Quebec to fight the British brought with it typhus; Gaultier contracted it and died (*Dictionary of Canadian Biography Online*).

Herbal medicinal literature extols its many virtues for all manner of ills and describes the berries being used as a tea, but repeatedly cautions that it is 'not to be taken internally'. The cautions may refer to the oil, for while the berries are reported as harmless, the oil produced by steam distillation is almost pure methyl salicylate and has caused death when ingested or applied too generously to the skin (Frohne, 2004). Small amounts are added to toothpastes. ∎

In the family Ericaceae, *Gaultheria procumbens* is a slow growing, dwarf, evergreen shrub which thrives in North American forests. In the Medicinal Garden it edges a raised bed where it brightens the border in the coldest months with its shiny, red, aromatic berries. Male and female flowers are born on separate plants, so both are necessary to produce the fruits. In spring and summer pink-tinged white, bell-shaped flowers appear. Like other members of the family Ericaceae, it requires humus-rich, acidic soil. It is fully hardy, but prefers a sheltered site and does not like to dry out. We keep it well watered in summer and mulch annually with leaf mould in spring.

Red berries of Gaultheria procumbens

Gaultheria procumbens

Gentiana asclepiadea

Gentiana asclepiadea Gentius, King of Illyria

This popular genus of garden plants is named after Gentius, King of Illyria (the western Balkan Peninsula) in 181–168 BC.

Gentius had a powerful navy of 270 warships (lembi) and like most kings of this era he fought constant wars, fighting with the Romans against Macedonia, and then changing sides only to be defeated and brought captive to Rome in 168 BC. The species name of *G. asclepiadea* refers to Asclepius, the Greek god of medicine (qv *Asclepias tuberosa*, p26).

Woodcut of *Gentiana lutea* from Mattioli (1569)

Gentius 'discovered' the medicinal value of the root of *Gentiana lutea* according to Dioscorides, who recommends it for animal bites, sprains, healing wounds and (as a pessary) as an abortifacient. Later authors note its bitter taste, and quote Galen as thus indicating its use as a purgative. Culpeper (1649) writes:

> ... some call it Felwort or Baldmoney. It is ... a notable counterpoison, it opens obstructions, helps the bitings of venomous beasts, and mad dogs, helps digestion, and cleanseth the body of raw humours; our chyrugians [surgeons] use the root in the form of a tent to open the sore, they are also very profitable for ruptures [hernias] or such as are burnt.

The root is still used as the bittering agent in Angostura bitters, the basis for a 'Pink Gin', and in herbal medicine for everything from malaria to snakebite. It is not the source of Gentian violet, a blue-purple dye, which is derived from coal tar. ∎

> A member of the Gentianaceae family, it is a hardy perennial hailing from the woodlands of central and southern Europe. It has tall, graceful stems with blue-green leaves and produces tubular, dark blue flowers in late summer. It prefers a shady position in free-draining, damp soil. The roots may rot in cold, wet winter conditions. Once planted, it is best left undisturbed with an annual mulch of leaf mould. Plants can be propagated by sowing fresh seed in a cold frame or by careful division.

Greyia sutherlandii flowering in Natal © Peter Croeser

Greyia sutherlandii Peter Cormack Sutherland

This, the Natal Bottlebrush, comes from South Africa and is named after the physician Dr Peter Cormack Sutherland (1822–1900). He was born in Scotland, and studied medicine and geology.

In 1850 he was the ship's surgeon, sailing in HMS *Sophia*, to discover the fate of Sir John Franklin's ill-fated expedition (1845) with HMS *Erebus* and HMS *Terror*, which had been lost in the Arctic. Frozen into the ice in Assistance Bay to the south of Cornwallis Island in HMS *Sophia* with her companion ship HMS *Lady Franklin* and the schooner *Felix*, they sent out long-distance sledging parties looking for the lost men. They never found Franklin or the ships, only the graves of some of the crew on King William Island. He wrote an account in *Journal of a voyage in Baffin's Bay and Barrow Straits* (2 vols, 1852), which included plants collected. He brought back 88 zoological specimens, 26 plants, 80 minerals and 30 fossils, which were deposited at the Royal Navy Hospital Museum at Haslar. He is described as 'a most indefatigable officer, and his attention while on board to natural history and meteorology will no doubt afford many useful facts'. He also wrote the meteorology and geology section of Sir Edward Inglefield's *A summer search for Sir John Franklin; with a peep into the Polar Basin* (1853).

Dr Peter Cormack Sutherland (1822–1900)
Courtesy of the Trustees of the Natal Society Foundation

Sutherland emigrated to Durban in 1853, where he set up in medical practice, but succeeded to the post of surveyor-general of Natal on the death of William Stanger in 1855. Later, in 1873, he designed a new town, Stanger, which he named after his predecessor. He named a hill, Garden Castle, after his second wife (Jane Garden Blaikie, married 1863). It was written of him that 'the span of his life was so long and the range of his interests so wide that his biography is virtually the history of Natal'. He was on the Natal legislative council, the first surgeon to the Military Volunteer Corps and chairman of the Natal Medical Committee (1856–96). He was a man of wide interests, from temperance to agriculture, natural history to education, who 'played a vigorous part in the intellectual atmosphere of the colonial capital' (Edington, 1963).

The genus name, *Greyia*, is for Sir George Grey (1812–98), a soldier, explorer and colonial administrator who was variously governor of South Australia, Cape Colony in South Africa, >

'He was on the Natal legislative council, the first surgeon to the Military Volunteer Corps and chairman of the Natal Medical Committee.'

Peter Sutherland was on the British brig *Sophia* which, with the brig *Lady Franklin* and the schooner *Felix*, overwintered in Assistance Bay. February 24, 1851, when the mercury thermometers froze (–38°). Image: © Wellcome Library, London

and of New Zealand, and latterly was premier of New Zealand. An interesting personage much involved with wars with the original inhabitants of these countries. He provided the money for Grey's Hospital in Pietermaritzburg in 1855, which was built under the supervision of Dr Sutherland.

The plant comes from South Africa, is a small tree up to seven metres high, with red flowers like a bottle-brush (*Calistemon*). The plant in the Medicinal Garden is still at the sapling stage and has yet to flower. Dr Sutherland introduced this tree to England as a garden plant, but in South Africa the wood is used to make household utensils. ■

Doctors in the Medicinal Garden

In the family Melianthaceae, *Greyia sutherlandii* is a frost-tender shrub found on inclines and upland crags up to 1,800 metres in South Africa. In the Medicinal Garden, with a thick layer of bark mulch for protection, it has survived two consecutive severe winters in a sheltered well-drained border. It can be propagated by cuttings from new growth in spring or by removal of rooted suckers. Pruning is not necessary, but it can be lightly trimmed after flowering if required.

Hacquetia epipactis
Balthasar (Belsazar) Hacquet

Balthasar Hacquet (1739/40–1815)
Image: ©Royal College of Physicians

This pretty little plant, with its golden flowers in late winter, is named for the Austrian physician, Balthasar (or Belsazar) Hacquet (1739/40–1815).

He studied medicine in Vienna and was a surgeon in the brutal Seven Years War (1756–63) – a world-wide war in which up to 1,400,000 people died. Later he was professor at the University of Lemberg (1788–1810). He wrote widely on many scientific disciplines including geology. His botanical work on the alpine flora of Carniola (now part of Slovenia) was the slim 16-page *Plantae alpinae Carniolicae* (1782) with beautiful engravings, now exceedingly rare.

It is a member of the Apiaceae family, along with Cow Parsley, *Anthriscus sylvestris*, but easily distinguished by its tiny size with umbels of golden flowers a mere half centimetre across, nesting on a rosette of leaves. It has no medicinal or herbal usage, but is a pleasant addition to a rockery, flowering in January. Genetic studies show it is in a clade with (ie closely related to) *Eryngium planum, Sanicula canadensis*, and *Astrantia major* (Downie *et al*, 1998). ■

Hacquetia epipactis is a slow-growing, hardy perennial ranging from mid to south-east Europe in woodlands, bearing diminutive, yellow flowers in early spring. In the Medicinal Garden it survives in raised beds of fertile, moist soil in partial shade with a mulch of leaf mould. Protection from slugs and snails is sometimes required. It can be propagated by division in spring.

Hacquetia epipactis

Halesia carolina Stephen Hales

Dr Stephen Hales DD FRS (1677–1761)
Image: © Royal College of Physicians

The snowbell tree, with its white bells and orange stamens in April, is named for Dr Stephen Hales DD FRS (1677–1761), a doctor of divinity. He came to Corpus Christi College, Cambridge, in 1696, graduated MA in theology in 1703 and became a fellow (1703–19), staying at Corpus Christi for 13 years.

This was an era when the concepts of Aristotle (that everything could be discovered by deduction) from 2,000 years before, were being replaced by mathematics, reason and experimentation led by Isaac Newton. In particular, Newton's book *Opticks* (1704), showing by experiment the properties of light, profoundly influenced him. He studied physics and chemistry, the rudiments of biology and did experiments on dogs (and much later on horses) 'in order to find out the real force of blood in the arteries'.

He was ordained and nominated perpetual curate of Teddington, Middlesex, in 1709, became rector of Porlock, Somerset, in 1718 and then of Faringdon, Hampshire, in 1723, and was made a doctor of divinity by Oxford in 1733. He was fascinated by how things worked – both animals and plants – and believed passionately in measurement and experiment. He continued with his experiments and was elected FRS in 1719 (March 1718 in the Gregorian calendar). Although the circulation of the blood around the body had been known since William Harvey's lectures in 1616 (published as *Exercitatio anatomica de motu cordis et sanguinis in animalibus* in 1628), the mechanism of the movement of sap in plants was still unknown until Hales published the results of his experiments in *Vegetable staticks* in 1727. >

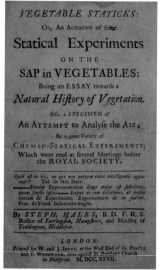

Title page of *Vegetable staticks* by Stephen Hales (1727)
Image: © Royal College of Physicians

'The mechanism of the movement of sap in plants was still unknown until Hales published the results of his experiments in *Vegetable staticks* in 1727.'

Halesia carolina

The interesting box-like seeds of *Halesia carolina*

He measured the weight of plants and the surface area of leaves to find how the water left the soil and was expired by the leaves, calculating the ratio of perspiration in man against the transpiration from leaves. He measured sap pressure (the first person to do this) by fastening a glass tube to the stump of a tree and seeing how high the sap went. He did much the same with dogs and horses, including connecting the femoral artery of a horse to a glass tube (using the trachea of a goose – in the absence of rubber tubing at this time) and measuring the height of the blood in the tube with a ruler (published in his *Haemostaticks* in 1733). His work on cutting off the heads of frogs to see how long the heart continued to beat, in 1730, much upset Dr Johnson who classed him with doctors who 'extend the art of torture'. His friend Alexander Pope (1688–1744) also complained about him dissecting dogs. Thomas Twining (1735–1804) wrote of him (Burchell, 1961):

> *... the good Pastor Stephen Hales*
> *Weighed moisture in a pair of scales*
> *To lingering death put mares and dogs*
> *And stripped the skin from living frogs ...*

In 1739, he was given the Copley medal by the Royal Society for his work on kidney and bladder stones and in 1753 he was elected to the French Academy of Sciences. In his parish he did good works in supplying Teddington with fresh water and campaigned against alcohol. In theological matters, he was appointed chaplain ('clerk of the closet') to the Princess Dowager Augusta of Wales in 1750. He was founder (1754) and vice-president of the Society for the Encouragement of Arts, Manufactures and Commerce (now the Royal Society of Arts), 'to support improvements in the liberal arts and sciences, and to stimulate enterprise for the common good'.

Halesia carolina is a small tree in the family Styracaceae. In the wild it can be found on wooded banks of streams and in the understory of woodlands in south-eastern USA. In the Medicinal Garden, it grows happily in moist, well-drained soil in a sunny, sheltered border. Hanging bell-shaped white flowers furnish the bare branches in spring before the leaves appear. It is mulched annually with well-rotted manure in early spring and overlong branches are pruned after flowering to maintain a balanced shape.

He invented a system of ventilating closed places to reduce the dangers of 'stale air', reported in *A description of ventilators* (1743), and *A treatise on ventilators* (1758). His windmill device was used in ships, prisons, hospitals and mines. He invented the surgical forceps and a gauge for measuring the depth of the sea, recommended that an upturned teacup in a pie dish stopped the pastry going soggy, devised a method for extracting bladder stones, observed the respiration of plants, and measured cardiac output in sheep. He was one of the great scientists of the first half of the 18th century (Burchell, 1961). *Halesia carolina* has no medicinal or ethnobotanical uses, but is a favoured small tree for moist acid soils. With its curious box-like seeds, which persist for the whole year, it provides an added interest to the Medicinal Garden. ■

Heimia salicifolia

Heimia salicifolia Ernst Ludwig Heim

This willow-leaved shrub with tiny yellow flowers is named after the German physician, amateur mycologist and botanist, Dr Ernst Ludwig Heim (1747–1834).

He qualified from Halle and became a physician in Berlin, popular for treating the poor free of charge. He was the doctor to Queen Louise of Prussia and taught the eight-year-old Alexander von Humboldt (the great plant explorer in Latin America). His medical advice to avoid indoor work and spend as much time as possible in the open (Lloyd *et al*, 1996) to the hypochondriacal Christian Sprengel (1750–1816) resulted in that taxonomist's career and his discovery (published 1793) that flowers are designed for the transmission of pollen by external vectors (eg insects and wind). Dr Heim is commemorated on a 1984 postage stamp. The plant grows from Texas and Mexico through Latin America. It is 'used in fertility control and the crushed leaves, fermented and drunk, act as a mildly intoxicating hallucinogen' which causes xanthopsia (everything appears yellow) (Mabberley, 2002).

Dr Ernst Ludwig Heim (1747–1834)
Image: © Wellcome Library, London

> **'The leaves, made into a tea, can induce visual and auditory hallucinosis but it is extremely bitter and causes vomiting.'**

In Argentina it is used as an antisyphilitic, sudorific, antipyretic, laxative and diuretic. It contains numerous alkaloids, some of which have weak antiprostaglandin synthetase activity. The leaves, made into a tea, can damage the brain and induce visual and auditory hallucinosis, but it is extremely bitter and causes vomiting. It may (possibly) be known as *sinucuichi* in Aztec herbalism. ■

> The willow-leaved *Heimia* in the family Lythraceae is a deciduous shrub found on river banks in southern USA, Mexico, Central America and the northern countries of South America. It bears numerous, bright-yellow flowers in late summer. It prefers a sheltered, sunny site with any well-drained soil. In severe winters, it may die back, but will recover from the base. A deep, bark mulch helps to protect it from frost.

Heuchera 'Silver Scrolls'
Johann Heinrich von Heucher

Johann Heinrich von Heucher (1677–1747)
Image: ©Royal Botanic Gardens, Kew

These North American woodland plants, locally called Alum Root, are named after Johann Heinrich von Heucher (1677–1747), professor of botany and medicine at Wittenburg University (1709), Germany, and later in Dresden.

Von Heucher was physician to King August II of Saxony. He was the founder of the botanic garden in Wittenburg and author of *Novi proventus horti medici Academiae Vitembergensis* (about the botanic garden) (1711). He was elected a fellow of the Royal Society in 1729. Most cultivars are derived from *Heuchera americana*.

Neither Austin (2004), Milspaugh (1974) nor Moerman (2009) record any uses by the Native Americans, but Henriette's herbal website, quoting *King's American dispensatory* (1898), says it is used to check diarrhoea, haemorrhage, skin ulcers, and as a pessary for vaginal discharge. ■

We grow the *Heuchera* cultivars, *Heuchera* 'Plum Pudding', *Heuchera* 'Silver Scrolls' and *Heuchera* 'Velvet Night'. They are semi-evergreen, hardy perennials in the family Saxifragaceae. The genus originates from North America and Mexico. They have attractive marbled, silvery or mottled lobed leaves and delicate, bell-shaped flowers, which form an eye-catching ground cover when planted *en masse*. We grow them in a raised bed of moist, free draining soil in partial shade. They do not like dry conditions so we water in dry spells and mulch with well-rotted manure in early spring avoiding the crowns. When the foliage becomes untidy, it can be cut down and will soon be replaced by new growth.

Heuchera 'Velvet Night'

Doctors in the Medicinal Garden

Heuchera 'Silver Scrolls'

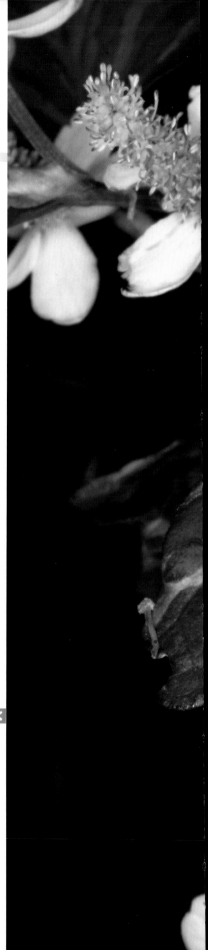

Houttuynia cordata 'Boo-Boo'
Maarten (Martinus) Houttuyn

Houttuynia cordata, the Chameleon or Lizard Plant, is named for Maarten (Martinus) Houttuyn (1720–98), the Dutch naturalist and physician from Hoorn, Netherlands.

His 37-volume work *Natuurlyke historie* (1761–85) demonstrated an encyclopaedic knowledge of natural history. He followed in the footsteps of his father, Dr Willem Houttuyn, and qualified at Leiden in 1749. From 1757–65, Houttuyn translated foreign medical papers published in the 10-volume *Uitgezogte verhandelingen* ('Selected papers'). He spoke many languages, but preferred speaking in Latin with foreigners. His other publications are numerous and it is unlikely that he found time to practise as a doctor. His 'cabinet of curiosities', the zoological specimens, was auctioned in 1787 and the botanical specimens in 1789.

   Houttuynia cordata is used in traditional Chinese herbal medicine, and in Japan as a tonic tea, *dokudami-cha*, and for chronic earache. The plants we grow at the Medicinal Garden are the cultivars 'Boo-Boo' and 'Joker's Gold' with multicoloured leaves, variants of the wild form whose leaves are just green. ∎

This hardy, perennial member of the Saururaceae family is native to moist woodlands and marshy areas from the east Himalayas to Japan. It prefers to grow in rich, damp soil in sun or partial shade. At the Medicinal Garden we grow its cultivars in pots on a sunny terrace. It has aromatic heart-shaped leaves and small white flowers. Stock can be easily increased by dividing clumps in spring.

Houttuynia cordata 'Boo-Boo'

Knautia macedonica

Knautia macedonica Christof and Christian Knaut

This honours the brothers Knaut: Christof Knaut (also Knauth, 1638–94) and his brother Christian Knaut (1654–1716).

Christof Knauth was a German doctor, botanist, professor at Halle, and author of *Enumeratio plantarum circa halam Saxonum … sponte provenientium* (1687). His brother Christian – author of *Methodus plantarum genuina* (1716), a pre-Linnaean classification of flowering plants – was also a botanist, physician and librarian. Christian studied medicine at the University of Leipzig and gained his doctorate from the University of Jena in 1682. He worked as the physician and librarian to Prince Manuel Lebrecht of Anhalt-Köthen. Christof was 16 years older than Christian, and some authors (eg Thomas, 1901) state that they were father and son. In the absence of birth certificates, I prefer to accept the fraternal relationship than to have Christian conceived when Christof was 15 years old.

The plant was traditionally used as a compress in its native Balkans to relieve dermatitis and itching. This use is a local survival of what was once a widespread application of this plant and its relations, and is an example of the doctrine of signatures in which the therapeutic benefit of a plant is suggested by some aspect of its anatomy; it has rough-textured leaves, so it was supposed to cure rough, itchy skin. It was locally called 'Scabious' and 'Widow Flower', the former because, like the genus *Scabious*, it was expected to cure scabies and itching. ∎

METHODUS PLANTARUM GENUINA,

QVA

NOTAE CHARACTERISTICÆ SEU DIFFERENTIÆ GENERICÆ TAM SUMMÆ, QVAM SUBALTERNÆ ORDINE DIGERUNTUR ET PER TABULAS, QVAS VOCANT, SYNOPTICAS PERSPICUE DELINEANTUR;

IN GRATIAM STUDIOSÆ JUVENTUTIS ADORNATA ATQVE EDITA

A

CHRISTIANO KNAUT MED. DOCT. ARCHIATRO ANHALTINO ET BIBLIOTHECARIO HALENSI.

LIPSIÆ ET HALÆ, Proſtat in Officina ADAMI SELLII, M DCC XVI.

Title page of Christian Knaut's *Methodus plantarum* (1716)
Image: © Royal Botanic Gardens, Kew

> This fully hardy perennial in the family Caprifoliaceae hails from woods and scrub of central Europe. In the Medicinal Garden from July to September, its beautiful, deep-purple pompom flowers mingle with other European wild flowers in a warm, sunny, free draining border, where they are loved by bees and butterflies. Due to a sprawling habit, it benefits from staking in spring when the foliage begins to appear. A mulch of well-rotted manure is applied annually; it is watered during dry spells and cut down in autumn when the foliage begins to look untidy.

Kniphofia caulescens

Kniphofia caulescens
Johann (Johannes) Hieronymus Kniphof

A spectacular red-hot poker from South Africa which commemorates Johann Hieronymus Kniphof (1704–63), professor of medicine at Erfurt University in Germany.

Dr Johann Hieronymus Kniphof (1704–63)
Image: © Royal College of Physicians, London

He was famous for his 10-volume work *Botanica in originali seu herbarium vivum in quo plantarum ...* (1759–64), which contained 1,189 pictures of plants each produced by coating the plant in (black) printer's ink and then pressing it carefully onto the paper to produce a life-size image. These were then coloured by hand. Like a herbarium specimen, if the plant was too large for the page then the stem would be cut and it would be displayed in two parts. The whole process was hugely laborious and each specimen could only be used to make five prints, so thousands of plants were needed – and of course the pages could only be printed when the plants were in flower. Only 10 complete copies are known to have survived. This was the first botanical atlas to use the Linnaean system of classification.

Kniphofia are pollinated by birds and insects. They have been used in 'muthi' medicine as a snake repellent and for chest complaints, but they contain toxic chemicals, knipholone compounds, and should not be eaten. ■

Kniphofia caulescens, a perennial in the family Asphodelaceae, hails from South Africa. In late summer, at the front of a sunny, well-drained border, it produces spikes of orange-flushed, cream flowers against glaucous leaves. Despite being borderline frost-hardy, it survives outside with an annual mulch of bark for protection.

Lavatera olbia Jean Rodolphe Lavater

The Tree Mallow is named after J(ean) R(odolphe) Lavater, 17th century physician and naturalist from Zurich, according to Stearn's *Dictionary of plant names for gardeners* (1996). Publication evidence shows he was active in 1700–8.

He is a very difficult person to trace, not helped by Lavater being a common name in Zurich at the time and biographers not doing their homework. The name *Lavatera* for a mallow was first used by Joseph Pitton de Tournefort (1656–1708) in 1706. That our Dr Lavater was alive at the time and a contemporary of Tournefort, is clear in a letter from James Petiver FRS (1663–1718), apothecary of London, dated 21 April 1708 to Joan Salvador, in which he writes: 'I desire Sir, you will acquaint Dr Tournefort when you write to him, that I was in expectation of receiving something [plants] from him by the hands of our Curious Freind [sic] Dr Lavater a Swiss who was lately with him … '. The only physician with those initials and in that era, Johannes Rodolphus (Johan Rudolf/Jean Rodolphe) Lavater, wrote a bibliography of the natural history of Switzerland,

Woodcut of *Althea arborea olbia* from L'Obel (1571)

Historiae Helveticae naturalis prolegomena: publicae eruditorum syzetesei subjecta/praeside J. Jacobo Scheuchzero; respondente Johanne Rodolfo Lavatero (1700). He was elected a fellow of the Royal Society in November 1708.

David Gledhill in *The names of plants* (2008) says it was named for the 'brothers Lavater, eighteenth century Swiss naturalists', but I can find no source for fraternal Swiss botanists with that name. There was a Swiss physician and naturalist, Johann Heinrich Lavater (1611–91), who corresponded with the botanist Pierre Magnol in France, but, being dead, he could not have been the companion of Tournefort referred to by Petiver in 1708. Our Lavater cannot be the famous physiognomist and poet, Johann Kaspar Lavater (1741–1801) from Zurich, who was not born in 1706. The two theologians from Zurich >

'The roots … are useful for clearing up "dangerous greene wounds … it helpeth digestion in them and bringeth old ulcers to maturation".'

Lavatera olbia

'Linnaeus described *Lavatera olbia* in *Species plantarum* (1753), giving its habitat as "Habitat in Olbia insula Galloprovincia" (found in the Iles d'Hyères, an island in [the south of] France).'

called Johann Rudolf Lavater (1579–1625 and 1695–1761), are the wrong era to be the 'Curious Freind'. References are very hard to find, but there are some minutes of a city council meeting in Bremgarten, on 7 April 1693, which are principally taken up by a dispute as to whether Johann Rudolf Lavater from Zurich or Johann Karl Balthasar from Luzern should take the minutes. The date makes it impossible for it to have been either of our theologians, or the physiognomist, so it may be a clue to our JR Lavater's other interests.

Linnaeus described *Lavatera olbia* in *Species plantarum* (1753), giving its habitat as '*Habitat in* Olbia *insula* Galloprovincia' (found in the Iles d'Hyères, an island in [the south of] France), separating it from *Malva* and *Althaea* as the genus had been known previously.

Linnaeus based *Lavatera olbia* on the plant described two centuries previously as A*lthea arborea olbia* in L'Obel's *Stirpium adversaria nova* (L'Obel and Pena, 1570/1) renamed *Althea frutex* in his *Plantarum* (L'Obel, 1576). He raised it in the garden, in Coleman Street, London, of Hugh Morgan the Apothecary to Queen Elizabeth I. As the owner of the garden in which *Lavatera olbia* was first raised, Hugh Morgan deserves a short note, for he also features in the *Annals of the College of Physicians*, which record his being censured for dealing in medicines (1556) and selling pills without a doctor's permission (1559). Over 20 of the plants mentioned by L'Obel came from his garden. In later years he had a garden in Battersea, mentioned by Parkinson (1629), and died there in 1613 at the age of 103 years (Raven, 1947).

The English name, Tree Mallow, persists. Gerard writes that the leaves as a poultice are analgesic and, as a tea, help relieve the pain of renal stones; the roots, boiled in water with various other plants are useful for (among much else) clearing up 'dangerous greene wounds … it helpeth digestion in them and bringeth old ulcers to maturation'. The marshmallow of confectionery was derived from the root of *Althaea officinalis,* the marshmallow, but is now made of sugars, corn syrup and gelatin with various flavourings. ∎

Lavatera olbia is a shrub originating from the western Mediterranean in the family Malvaceae. It grows at the Medicinal Garden in a well-drained, sunny raised bed. In summer, it produces masses of pink flowers on long arching branches against silvery-grey leaves. It is watered in dry spells and pruned hard in late spring to encourage new flower shoots. No feeding is necessary as this may inhibit flowering.

Lavatera arborea from Sowerby (1832–46)

Lavatera arborea.

Jan.1.1808. Publish'd by Jas Sowerby London.

Lilium henryi

Lilium henryi Augustine Henry

This commemorates Dr Augustine Henry (1857–1930) who collected plants in China and Taiwan while working for Britain's Imperial Customs Service.

Augustine Henry (1857–1930)
Image: © Royal Botanic Gardens, Kew

He discovered this orange-flowered lily in his travels. He was of Irish stock, and was educated in Ireland, but qualified in medicine in Edinburgh and became a fluent speaker of Chinese. He arrived in Shanghai in 1881 and from 1882–9 he was assistant medical officer in Yichang. He collected extensively in Szechuan and Hubei. He was posted to the island of Huinan (modern-day Hainan), where he collected 750 plants, but was invalided home with malaria. He was transferred to Taiwan (1892–4) where he made further collections and published *Notes on economic botany in China* (1893). He returned to England, studied law and became a member of the Middle Temple, but after a year returned to China as acting chief commissioner of customs from 1895–1900. He continued collecting. In total, he sent back 15,000 herbarium specimens and 500 plants to Kew, from which 25 new genera and 500 new species were described, but it was EH Wilson who later sent back living specimens of these plants. The next two years were spent at Kew and at the French National School of Forestry at Nancy, during which he commenced to co-author (with HJ Elwes) *Trees of Great Britain and Ireland* (7 vols, 1913). He became professor of forestry at Cambridge University, (1907–13), then professor of forestry at the Royal College of Science (merged into University College in 1926), Dublin, until his retirement in 1927. His personal herbarium of 10,000 specimens was bequeathed to the National Botanic Gardens, Glasnevin.

Parthenocissus henryi

Henry brought *Lilium henryi* with him when he left Yichang in 1889 and gave some to Charles Ford, who forwarded some to Kew. It is widely cultivated today and is lime-tolerant. Hybrids with the 'Trumpet' lilies produced the line of late-blooming 'Sunburst' lilies. We also grow *Rubus henryi* var *bambusarum* and the creeper, *Parthenocissus henryi*. ∎

Lilium henryi is a bulbous perennial in the family Liliaceae originating from China. It is planted deeply in a well-drained, fertile raised bed under trees, where it produces tall stems of lightly scented, orange, spotted, Turk's-cap style flowers in late summer. The stems are lax so they may benefit from staking. In early spring, they are mulched with well-rotted manure.

Lindera benzoin

Lindera benzoin Johan (Linder) Lindestolpe

The genus name of *Lindera benzoin*, the Spicebush, was created by Carl Peter Thunberg in 1783 after Johan Lindestolpe (1678–1724), Swedish botanist and physician, born Johan Linder, and incorrectly, also called Johann Linder.

He was born in Karlstad in 1678 and died in Stockholm in 1724, the dates being those given by the National Library of Sweden and not 1676–1723 as given elsewhere. He studied at first in Åbo and Uppsala, then went abroad and entered (was matriculated at) the University of Harderwijk on 22 September 1706. His dissertation *De foeda lue dicta venerea* (Thoughts about the infectious French disease, 1705) is the earliest explicit description of syphilis published in Sweden. He became a doctor of medicine there and published a dissertation in Leiden, *Liber de venenis in genere* ... (1708, concerning poison). From 1709–10, he served as a doctor in the Swedish navy's Ingermanländ fleet, following which he was in medical practice in Stockholm. In 1719, he was appointed an assessor in the medical school and ennobled, changing his name to Lindestolpe. He also wrote *Tanckar och anmärckningar öfwer desze tijders pestilentia* (1711); the *Flora wiksbergensis* (1716); *Swenska färge-konst, med inländske örter, ... och mineralier* (1720); and *Tanckar om skörbugg och rogfubben* (1721); and much else on meteorology, geology and medicine. His first marriage was to Anna Margareta Örn, and his second in 1720 to Lady (baroness) Eva Christina Cronhielm. They had no surviving children.

Lindera benzoin is known as Spicebush because it was used for flavouring strong-tasting meats by the North American Cherokee and Ojibwa. Medicinally it was used for a wide variety of conditions, for which it is unlikely to have had any effect. The Cherokee used it for blood disorders (although it is impossible to know what was meant by this), female problems, colds, croup, measles and tuberculosis. The Mohegans used it to kill intestinal worms (Austin, 2004). ■

Lindera benzoin in the family Lauraceae is native to the wooded slopes and streams of south-east Canada and eastern USA. A hardy, deciduous shrub, its greenish-yellow flowers appear on bare branches in spring followed by aromatic leaves, bright-red fruit and yellow autumn colour. It prefers moist, acidic soil so is mulched annually with leaf mould and fed with a seaweed-based fertiliser during the growing season. We prune it in spring only to remove dead and damaged wood, but it can be cut back hard to the base if necessary.

Listera ovata Martin Lister

This is the Common Twayblade (now *Neottia ovata*), a rather dull European orchid. It was named after Dr Martin Lister FRCP FRS (1639–1712), physician to Queen Anne.

He was born in Buckinghamshire, gained an arts degree at St John's College, Cambridge, in 1658, and then an MA in 1662. He studied medicine, travelling in France until 1670, and on his return set up practice in York. He was much involved with natural history and antiquities, and was elected FRS in November 1671. His *Historiae conchyliorum*, published in 1685 (an encyclopaedia of shells with 1,000 drawings made by his daughters Susanna and Mary), was regarded as opening a new era in the science of conchology. He decided to move to London, and was created a doctor of medicine at Oxford in 1683. He was admitted as a candidate of the (Royal) College of Physicians in 1684 and created a fellow in 1687. He served as a censor at the (Royal) College of Physicians in 1694. He became physician to Queen Anne, Queen of England (Scotland, Ireland and France) who reigned 1702–14, in 1709. He wrote papers on subjects from spiders to geology which were published in the *Proceedings of the Royal Society.*

This orchid is found throughout northern Europe and Asia, and in North America (on an island in Lake Huron, Ontario). It is pollinated by *Cantharis rufipes* beetles. It was used for treating wounds and ruptures (Lyte, 1578; Fuchs, 1551; Johnson, 1633) but does not appear in modern medical herbals and has no medicinal value. It first appeared as *Ophris* in Leonart Fuchs' herbal *De historia stirpium* (1542) and as *Bifolium* in Dodoens' *Cruydeboeck* (1554), where it is illustrated and described with *Neottia nidus-avis,* the saprophytic Bird's Nest orchid. Linnaeus called it *Ophrys ovata* (1753); Robert Brown called it *Listera* in 1813; Bluff and Fingerhuth called it *Neottia* in 1838, but it remained as *Listera* until recently when taxonomists agreed with Dodoens and accepted it as *Neottia ovata.* ■

The beetle, *Cantharis rufipes,* pollinating *Listera ovata.* Note the pollen attached to its head

This British native orchid ranges from Europe to central Asia (with one colony in the USA) in damp meadows and woodlands. From May to July, spikes of green hooded flowers appear between two broad leaves just above ground level. We grow them in a raised bed in fertile, moist soil in the dappled shade of a large plane tree, where it benefits from an annual mulch of leaf mould. During dry periods in the growing season, it is watered regularly. Otherwise, as with most terrestrial orchids, it is best left undisturbed.

Listera ovata

Lobelia tupa Matthias de L'Obel (Lobel)

The genus was named after Matthias de L'Obel or Lobel (1538–1616), Flemish botanist and physician to James I of England.

The family name of L'Obel derives from the French word for the white poplar, '*aubel*'. He was born in Rijsel near Lille in northern France, studied medicine at Leuven (Louvain), where Dodoens studied 20 years previously, and both medicine and botany at Montpelier University (1565– *c.* 1568), where he was taught by perhaps the most famous teacher of the age, Guillaume Rondelet, regius professor of medicine. Rondelet was so impressed with L'Obel that he gave him all his books. Here L'Obel met Pierre Pena. They came to England in 1569 in the reign of Queen Elizabeth I (1533–1603), and travelled together collecting native plants. When Pena returned to the Continent in 1571 to practise medicine, L'Obel, who had married an Englishwoman, stayed in England for a few months longer. When he returned to the Low Countries (the Netherlands) he practised medicine in Antwerp and then Delft from 1571 to 1581, returning to Antwerp where he became physician to William the Silent, Prince of Orange. After the latter's assassination in 1584, he returned to England and became superintendent of the garden of Lord Zouche in Hackney. He helped John Gerard publish his herbal (in 1597), an English translation of Dodoens' herbal, correcting Gerard's many mistakes and identifying the woodcuts – the majority of which had been used in the earlier herbals of Fuchs, Mattioli, Dodoens and his own books. In 1606, he became physician and botanist to James I (King of England, 1603–25) and thereafter remained in England, living with his married daughter in Highgate until his death. He was buried at the church of St Denis, Highgate (Greene, 1983).

He is best known as the author, with Pierre Pena, of the herbal *Nova stirpium adversaria* (1570/1) published by Thomas Purfoot of London while they were still in England. This was followed by his beautifully illustrated *Plantarum seu Stirpium Historia* (1576) published by Christopher Plantin of Antwerp, when L'Obel was back in the Netherlands. They can be regarded as a two-volume work as the index to the second edition of the *adversaria* covers both books. In these they produced one of the earliest classifications of plants, grouping them primarily by leaf structure, which resulted in them separating monocotyledons from dicotyledons, although he did not use these terms. For people seeking identification of a plant, all the plants with similar leaf structure – for example, *Ranunculus, Aconitum, Helleborus, Geranium, Ricinus, Levisticum* with heavily dissected leaves – were grouped together so could be readily compared. This was in marked contrast to Leonhart Fuchs (in 1542) and William Turner (in 1551–68) whose herbals arrange the plants more or less in alphabetical order of their Latin names. In all they described 1,500 species, with >

Lobelia tupa

Lobelia siphilitica.

Published by D.ʳ Woodville. Jan.ʸ 1.1791.

Lobelia siphilitica illustrated in Woodville's *Medical botany* (1790), where the story of its purchase is recounted

their medicinal uses in the *Stirpium adversaria,* but in the *Plantarum* L'Obel increased the number of woodcuts from 268 to over 2,000 – mostly obtained from the printers of the works of L'Escluse, Dodoens and Mattioli. Linnaeus (1753) has always been credited with introducing the binomial system of genus + species for naming plants, but L'Obel and the other herbalists were already doing this. L'Obel's Latin index often gave the genus name and author, with frequent binomials, sometimes also with the author, eg *Moly Hippocratis; Moly Plin[y]; Mentha tertia Dod[onaeus]*. In 1581, L'Obel published his *Kruydtboeck* in Flemish with 2,181 woodcuts and 1,306 pages, and *Plantarum seu stirpium icones* (pictures only), but referenced to where the descriptions could be found in his earlier works. The *Icones* was heavily quoted by Linnaeus in 1753.

The decorative *Lobelia cardinalis*

Lobelia tupa has fiery red flower scapes, but it was the leaves which were smoked by the Mapuchu Indians of Chile for their rather special effects (not recommended!). We also grow the scarlet *L. cardinalis* in the Medicinal Garden and the sky-blue *L. siphilitica.* The latter was sold as a 'secret cure' to gullible British colonists by Native Americans as a cure for syphilis. William Woodville writes (1790):

> *It derived the name* siphilitica *from its efficacy in the cure of syphilis, as experienced by the North American Indians, who considered it a specific in that disease, and with whom it was long an important secret. The secret was purchased by Sir William Johnson ... We do not find that the antisyphilitic powers of the* Lobelia *have been confirmed by any instances of European practice.*

Sir William Johnson (1715–74) farmed land and set up a trading post in New York province in the territory of the Mohawks, with whom he had a good relationship. John Lindley also noted (1838) '... European practice does not confirm its American reputation'.
The active ingredient in *Lobelia* is lobeline, which has a similar action to nicotine and was used for a while for asthma and to help people to stop smoking. Sadly, it was no more effective in this than it was for syphilis. ■

In the family Campanulaceae, *Lobelia tupa* is an erect perennial from Chile. Striking red flower spikes appear against velvety grey-green leaves in late summer. In the Medicinal Garden, it grows well in a sheltered sunny position in fertile, moist soil. Our plants have been prone to the pest red spider mite, which is less of a problem in a position with good air circulation and regular misting in dry weather.

Lonicera fragrantissima Adam Lonitzer (Lonicerus)

This shrubby, fragrant, white-flowered honeysuckle is named for Adam Lonitzer (Lonicerus) (1528–86).

Adam Lonitzer (1528–86)
Image: © Royal College of Physicians

A German botanist, physician and author of the botanical herbal *Naturalis historiae opus novum* (vol 1 in 1551, vol 2 in 1555) and its German translation, the *Kreuterbuch* (1557) (sourced mainly from earlier herbals), he became professor of mathematics at the University of Marburg in 1553 and doctor of medicine in 1554, working in Frankfurt-am-Main. His wife was the daughter of the Frankfurt publisher, Christian Egenolff, who published his book along with other herbals. Adam's father, Johann Lonitzer (Joanne Lonicerus) (1499–1569), was professor of theology and ancient languages and contributed the Greek, Hebrew, Latin and German names of plants to Ruellio's commentary on Dioscorides (edition of 1543) published by Egenolff.

Lonicera fragrantissima was introduced to Europe from China in the early 1840s by the British plant collector Robert Fortune, working for the Royal Horticultural Society. We also grow *Lonicera periclymenum*, our familiar climbing honeysuckle, but the honeysuckle of Dioscorides may have been *Lonicera etrusca,* which he called *clymenon*. He recommended the fruit, dried and drunk in wine for 40 days, to 'reduce the spleen, abate fatigue, orthopnea [breathlessness on lying flat], and hiccoughs, but from the sixth day it makes the urine bloody' (Beck, 2005). Dioscorides also reported that it speeded up labour, made people sterile after drinking it for 37 days, and reduced the shivering of intermittent fevers if rubbed on with olive oil. Dioscorides is clearly indicating that the berries are poisonous and there must be few people who would put up with haematuria for over a month to cure hiccoughs. Johnson (1633), using the name *Periclymenum*, woodbinde or honisuckles, repeats Dioscorides, but adds that the flowers stop 'pissing of blood' and can be used for soreness of the throat and 'the secret parts'. Modern literature (Frohne, 2004) reports that honeysuckles are poisonous and herbals note the induction of vomiting with berries, and purgation with the leaves – a sure sign of toxicity. Sucking the nectar from the flowers appears acceptable. ■

Originating from China, in the Caprifoliaceae family, *Lonicera fragrantissima* is a hardy, semi-evergreen winter-flowering honeysuckle. In the Medicinal Garden it grows well in a deep, raised bed of fertile soil in the partial shade of a plane tree. It is mulched annually with well-rotted manure and pruned in spring after flowering by removing older wood to the base.

Lonicera fragrantissima

Matthiola incana Pietro Andrea Mattioli

Pietro Andrea Mattioli (1500/1–77)
Image: © Royal College of Physicians.

Matthiola incana is the Latin name for the summer-flowering garden 'Ten-week Stocks'. It commemorates Pietro Andrea Mattioli (1500/1–77), physician and botanist, whose name is Latinised to Matthiolus.

He was born on 23 March 1500 in the old Gregorian calendar (1501 using the modern system), in Siena, Italy, and died of the plague in Trento. He gained his MD from Padua in 1523 and practised medicine in Italy and Austria as the physician to Archduke Ferdinand II and to Maximillian II, the Holy Roman emperor. The study of plants was a major part of medicine, and Dioscorides' herbal, his six-part *Materia medica* from the 1st century AD, was the basis of medicinal practice. Mattioli published an Italian translation of Dioscorides, and in the same year a Latin version, with a commentary, *Commentarii in libros sex Pedacii Dioscoridis Anazarbei de medica materia* (1554). Like other writers of the time, he identified the plants of Dioscorides but also added in all the plants known to him. The detailed woodcuts of the later editions set a new standard; the books were incredibly popular and it is reported that 32,000 copies of the early editions were sold. He published other books including a poem on the Palace of the Cardinal of Trento, *Il magno Palazzo del Cardinale di Trento* (1539), one on the plague, *Remedia contra pestem* (1564), and on distillation of the sap of plants and preserving their taste and fragrance, *Del modo di distillare le acque da tutte le piante ...* (1604).

Matthiola incana appears as *Viola-matrionalis alba, V. punicea* and *V. purpurea* in Fuchs (1542), as *Leucoium purpureum et album* in Matthioli (1569) and Lobel (1576), typified by Linnaeus (1753) as *Cheiranthus incanus*, before being finally re-named *Matthiola incana* by William Aiton, at Kew, in 1812. They have clearly been in cultivation for at least 500 years in northern Europe. Whether this was the plant known to Dioscorides (AD 70) is uncertain, for he described it as white, quince-yellow or purple, and recommends it in baths for >

'Mattioli published an Italian translation of Dioscorides, and in the same year a Latin version, with a commentary, *Commentarii in libros sex Pedacii Dioscoridis Anazarbei de medica materia* (1554).'

Matthiola incana, a double flowered form

uterine disorders and to induce menstruation. The ground-up roots applied as a poultice were, he writes, good for the spleen and for gout (Beck, 2005). It may be that the yellow flowers of Dioscorides were those of the not dissimilar wallflower, *Erysimum cheiri*. Fuchs noted them as garden plants which, soaked in water (presumably hot) whose vapour was then inhaled, would help those with convulsions, breathing difficulties and chronic cough, stimulate urine and menstruation, and induce sweating.

It is in the cabbage family, Brassicaceae. Our plants come from commercial seed packets and contain a mixture of single and double forms. The latter are sterile, but selective breeding has increased the proportion of double forms from the seed of single forms to as much as 80%.

Matthiola incana as Leucoium album & purpureum in Matthioli (1569)

'Ten-week Stocks' are popular garden annuals, flowering in the year of sowing, whereas 'Brompton Stocks' (another variety of *M. incana*) are biennials, flowering the following year. There are numerous cultivars. Johnson (1633), calling them Stocke Gillofloures or *Leucoium*, notes the white and purple forms, singles and doubles. About their medicinal value he writes, 'not used in Physicke except among certain Empiricks and Quacksalvers, about love and lust matters, which for modestie I omit'. The thought of a member of the cabbage family being an aphrodisiac might encourage the gullible to take more seriously the government's plea to eat five portions of vegetable/fruit per day. ∎

Originating from sandy and rocky seaside areas of the Mediterranean, *Matthiola incana* is a fragrant annual or biennial in the Brassicaceae family. It prefers to grow in fertile soil in full sun. Seed should be sown under glass in early spring and planted out after frosts are past, or outdoors in June or July. Young plants are overwintered in an unheated glasshouse or cold frame to flower in summer the following year. It sometimes continues as a short-lived perennial if conditions are favourable.

Matthiola incana illustrated in Sowerby (1832–46) has been a popular garden annual for two centuries

Matthiola incana.

Monarda didyma 'Violet Queen'

Monarda didyma 'Violet Queen'
Nicolás Bautista Monardes

The bee-balm and bergamot commemorates Nicolás Bautista Monardes (1512–88), physician and botanist from Seville, son of an Italian bookseller and one of the most distinguished physicians of his day (Guerra, 1961).

He entered the University of Alcalá de Henares, where he obtained a degree in the arts in 1530 and his medical degree in 1533. He had his practice in Seville, at its University from 1547. While most biographers (Barnhart, 1965) give the year of his birth as 1493, this seems unlikely and 1512 is given in the catalogue of the Biblioteca Nacional de Lisboa (Lavoura, 2001) and by other bibliographic sources. It is to Monardes that we owe early information about medicinal plants from the New World, published in three parts (1569, 1571, 1574), the first one being *Dos libros, el uno que trata de todas las cosas que se traen de nuestras Indias Occidentales, que sirven al uso de la Medicina, y el otra que trata de la Piedra Bezaar, y la Yerua Escuerçonera* (two books, one which deals with all the things which come from West Indies, which are of use in medicine, and the other which deals with the bezoar stone and the herb called Escorzonera (*Scorzonera hispánica* or *Scorzonera humilis*)). The second book includes some of the earliest information on tobacco; it was translated into English by John Frampton as *Joyfull Newes out of the newe founde Worlde* (1577). He describes tobacco being smoked by the Indians, but no English herbal in the next hundred years describes this usage. This new plant from Latin America was regarded as a wonderful panacea, and tobacco became known as *Herba sancta* – the holy plant – because of its supposedly curative virtues. Monardes was responsible for much of the enthusiasm for tobacco as a medicine. The sunflower appears here for the first time. Monardes also wrote a book expressing distrust of exotic drugs from the Americas, *Diálogo llamado pharmacodilosis* (1536), another on venesection in Greek and Arabic medicine, *De secanda vena in pleuriti inter Grecos et Arabes concordia* (1539), and about the medicinal properties of citrus fruits and roses, *De rosa et partibus eius* (1540). >

I efte quaderno en que ay dos tratados, y enel prime-ro fe trata de todas las cofas que fe traen de indias medi cinales. Y el fegundo que trata de ve-nenos y de fus remedios, efpecialmen-te de la piedra Bezaar, & de la yerua Efcuerçonera, y enel vno y enel otro no ay cofa de que fe ofenda nuefta fan &ta fee catholica y buenas coftûbres; antes lo tengo por muy vtil & proue chofo, para doctos & indoctos, & por tal lo aprueuo. Fecho en doze de lu-nio, de mil & quinientos y feffenta & quatro años.

El Doctor Millan.

End page recommending Monardes' book (1569–74) on the medicines from the West Indies. Image: © Wellcome Library, London

Translation

'In this book there are two sections, the first deals with all the things with regard to the medicines of the Indies. The second deals with poisons and their remedies, especially the bezoar stone and the herb Escuerconera, and in the one and the other there are no things which offend our holy catholic church and moral customs, for they provide many uses and food, for doctors and patients, and because of this I approve of them. Written on the 12 June 1574. El Doctor Millan.'

Monarda fistulosa

'This new plant from Latin America was regarded as a wonderful panacea ... tobacco became known as *Herba sancta* – the holy plant – because of its supposedly curative virtues.'

In 1537 he married Catalina Morales, the daughter of Garcia Perez Morales, professor of medicine at Seville. They had seven children. In addition to his medical practice he had a business in importing drugs and in the slave trade – which later bankrupted him. After his wife's death in 1577 he became a cleric (*Complete dictionary of scientific biography*, 2008). He is reported to have died from a cerebral haemorrhage. If this was at the age of 95 it would have been extraordinary at that era in history. However, an examination of the ages at which he graduated and published make it likely that he was born around 1512, as proposed in the Biblioteca Nacional de Lisboa catalogue, and died aged 76. His works were published in 42 editions and in six languages.

The Oswego tribe of Native Americans used *Monarda didyma* as a tea on account of its fragrance, which resembles that of bergamot oil (which comes from *Citrus bergamia*). Austin (2004) reports it was used by the Creeks and Osage to cause perspiration, and to ward off rheumatism by the Alabama, Choctaw, Chickasaw and Creek. A tea made from the leaves was used to relieve headache by the Catawba, and the Osage also used it for pain relief and coughs, chest complaints and fevers. We also grow *M. fistulosa*, which, when first discovered, was described with an excellent drawing as *Origanum fistulosum canadense* in Cornut's *Canadensium plantarum historia* (1635). ∎

> **Monarda didyma** 'Violet Queen' and **M. fistulosa** in the family Lamiaceae are upright, hardy perennials which hail from North America. The brightly coloured flowers are popular with bees and butterflies when grown in a sunny border. They suffer in dry weather so we give them a good mulch of well-rotted manure in early spring and keep them well watered in summer.

Muehlenbeckia complexa var *triloba*
Heinrich Gustav Muehlenbeck or Mühlenbeck

Title page of Muehlenbeck's *Maladie des pommes de terre – krankheit der kartoffeln* (1845). Image: © Royal Botanic Gardens, Kew

Muehlenbeckia complexa, the aptly named Creeping Wire Vine, commemorates Dr Heinrich Gustav Muehlenbeck or Mühlenbeck (1798–1845), a physician from Mulhouse, France, who investigated the flora of Alsace.

He wrote on potato diseases *Maladie des pommes de terre – krankheit der kartoffeln* (in French and German, 1845). His vast herbarium, the Herbier Muehlenbeck, which consists of tens of thousands of specimens classified using the system of AP De Candolle (1824–74), has been deposited in the Louis Pasteur Herbarium of Strasbourg by the Société Industrielle de Mulhouse. A full catalogue has not been made, suffice it to say that it contains 20 plant families and 250 genera beginning with 'A'. Carl Daniel Friedrich Mieissner (1800–74), professor of botany at the University of Basel, just across the border from Mulhouse, named *Muehlenbeckia* after his contemporary and neighbour in 1841. Meissner was prolific in his publication of Australian genera, but neither he nor Muehlenbeck appear to have visited Australia or New Zealand.

This tangled creeper from New Zealand was the food for the moas, giant flightless birds, which were eaten into extinction by the indigenous peoples, aided by later settlers, thus upsetting any myth of living in harmony with nature. In South America, *M. sagittifolia* was used in the 19th century as a treatment for syphilis and liver abscesses (Hieronymus, 1882). ■

Muehlenbeckia complexa belongs to the family Polygonaceae and grows naturally in New Zealand in damp, fertile soils. In the Medicinal Garden, its creeping stems and miniature dark-green leaves make it an effective spreading ground cover in partially shaded borders. We only grow *M. complexa* var *triloba* with unusual violin-shaped leaves. It is trimmed as required to prevent it smothering neighbouring plants. Frost hardy, it benefits from an annual mulching with bark chips as protection.

Doctors in the Medicinal Garden

Muehlenbeckia complexa var triloba

Musa basjoo Antonius Musa

Banana plant from the West Indies, illustrated in Piso (1658)

The name of our semi-hardy banana which flowered in the Medicinal Garden in July 2009 has been linked to Antonius Musa (63–14 BC), physician to the first Roman emperor, Caesar Augustus.

He was the brother of Euphorbus, physician to King Juba II of Numidia after whom *Euphorbia* (qv) was named. Musa cured Augustus of 'congestion of the liver' with cold compresses, and of sciatica by beating the affected part with a stick. Augustus honoured him, exempting physicians from paying taxes, and a statue was erected in his honour near that of Aesculapius in Rome. 'Musa' is also the Arabic word for banana and 'basjoo' is a transliteration of the Japanese name for this banana, so the full name means 'Banana banana'.

While bananas are rich in protein and potassium, a staple food in the tropics, *Musa basjoo* produces no edible fruit. The main banana of commerce was *M. acuminata* 'Cavendish' a sterile, seedless, triploid cultivar, which is in danger of being wiped out by a *Fusarium* fungus in Asia. The search is on for equivalent cultivars that would be resistant to *Fusarium*. ■

'Augustus honoured him, exempting physicians from paying taxes, and a statue was erected in his honour near that of Aesculapius in Rome.'

Musa basjoo in the family Musaceae is a herbaceous perennial originating in the Far East and is the hardiest of banana plants. In a partially shaded, well-drained border it produces pendant spikes of cream flowers with brown bracts and very large, attractive, bright-green leaves which are prone to wind damage, so a sheltered site is preferred. In severe winters the plant may die back completely but will regrow from the base in spring. We give it generous layer of bark mulch or *Taxodium* needles around the crown for protection.

Musa basjoo flower and fruits

Paeonia officinalis

Paeonia officinalis Paeon

The glorious peony, commemorates Paeon, physician to the gods of ancient Greece, who enjoyed the best private practice of the era. Homer's *Iliad* v. 401 and 899 (*c.* 800 BC) provides further details (Murray, 1924).

Paeonia officinalis from Ruellio (1543)

The name Paeon came to be associated as being Apollo, Greek god of healing, poetry, the sun and much else, and father of Aesculapius/Asclepius. Hesiod, the greatest Greek author after Homer, about a century later, clearly regarded them as separate deities, viz:

> *If neither Phoebus Apollo does save us from death,*
> *nor Paean who knows remedies for everything.*

The Mycenaean Greeks of the late Bronze Age (1600–1100 BC) worshipped a god of healing called Paiawon, 'a divinity with a formidable knowledge of herbs and drugs ...' (Graf, 2009), and Apollo was not known. Paiawon's cult disappeared after the collapse of the Mycenaean world. The fusion of Paiawon/Paeon and Apollo occurred much later as both being names for the god of healing.

Theophrastus (*c.* 300 BC), repeated by Pliny (AD 79), wrote that if a woodpecker saw one collecting peony seed during the day, it would peck out one's eyes, and (like mandrake) the roots had to be pulled up at night by tying them to the tail of a dog, with the added warning that one's 'fundament might fall out' (anal prolapse) if one cut the roots with a knife. Theophrastus, I am glad to say, thought this 'far-fetched', as did Pliny, viz: 'all this, however, I take to be so much fiction, most frivolously invented to puff up their supposed marvellous properties'.

Dioscorides (AD 70) wrote that 15 of its black seeds, drunk with wine, were good for nightmares, uterine suffocation and uterine pains. Do not try this at home even if you know what uterine suffocation might be! >

'If a woodpecker saw one collecting peony seed during the day, it would peck out one's eyes, and (like mandrake) the roots had to be pulled up at night by tying them to the tail of a dog.'

1

2

3

4

Paeonia suffruticosa 'Chang Zhi Hong' is also grown in the Medicinal Garden

The roots, hung round the neck, were regarded as a cure for epilepsy for nearly 2,000 years, a belief which was incomprehensible until I found, in Elizabeth Blackwell's *A curious herbal* (1737), published with the approval of the Royal College of Physicians, that it was used to cure febrile fits in children, associated with teething (which stop whatever one does).

Paeonia suffruticosa was introduced to European horticulture by Sir Joseph Banks (1743–1820). A root extract in 25% alcohol has recently been licensed for use for the relief of menopausal hot flushing as an across-the-counter medication in Britain, despite inhibiting clotting mechanisms and causing uterine contractions, lack of toxicity, genotoxicity or genotoxicity trials, and the absence of proof that it works (MHRA website, 2011). ■

> ## 'The roots, hung round the neck, were regarded as a cure for epilepsy for nearly 2,000 years.'

The European *Paeonia officinalis*, a hardy perennial of the Paeoniaceae family, and the double form 'Rubra Plena' grow happily in the Medicinal Garden in a herbaceous border in dappled shade. The beautiful dissected foliage, crimson flowers from April to June and striking seed pods make it a welcome addition to the garden. Both this and *P. suffruticosa*, which we also grow, require deep, well-drained soil. The soil was prepared thoroughly before planting and the site was chosen carefully to avoid morning sun, which can cause damage after frost. We mulch annually with well-rotted manure in spring, avoiding the crowns. Otherwise, they are best left undisturbed.

Opposite page: *Paeonia officinalis* from Elizabeth Blackwell's *A curious herbal* (1737)

Phoenix theophrasti Theophrastus/Theophrastos

Theophrastus (371–287 BC)
Image: © Royal College of Physicians

This is the prickly-leaved, Cretan Date Palm which commemorates the Greek philospher/ botanist/herbalist Theophrastus/Theophrastos (371–287 BC) (his real name was Tyrtamus), the 'father of botany' who wrote on the medicinal properties of plants.

He was born at Eresos on the island of Lesbos and studied under Plato in Athens. When Aristotle was forced to flee Athens in 322 BC because of his support for the Macedonians, he gave his books and the leadership of the Lyceum (school) in Athens to Theophrastus, who continued there for 35 years until his death in AD 287. Theophrastus was the author of *Characters* (319 BC) which contains descriptions of moral types, and of *On the causes of plants* and *Enquiry into plants* (latter in two vols, Loeb edition, 1980), the two most important botanical books of antiquity. In book nine of the *Inquiry* (re *Juices of plants* and *Medicinal properties of plants*), Theophrastus discusses medicinal herbs. Here he gives the many uses of cyclamen including, 'they say also that the [ashes of the] root is a good charm for inducing rapid delivery and as a love potion'. When excavating the ruins of Pompey, a room was found which had been used as a pharmacy and contained cyclamen corms. It was noted that the local Italian workmen on the site would remove the cyclamen from the ground before excavating and take them home for 'medicinal purposes' – a tradition which Theophrastus had documented 2,300 years before (Jashemski, 1999). His classification of plants was, basically, trees, shrubs, under-shrubs and herbs with a subdivision (which was still used in part by Johnson in 1633) of cultivated and wild, with and without flowers, deciduous and evergreen. Volume two of the *Inquiry* also treats of perfumes, spices and the meteorological signs for rain, wind and fair weather.

Phoenix theophrasti is a small palm which, in limited places in the Mediterranean, forms small forests – unique among Europe's palms. The dates are edible but bitter and fibrous so of no commercial value. ■

This palm in the Arecaceae family is found from Crete to south-west Turkey. It has an orange trunk and erect, silvery-green, feathery leaf fronds with very spiky points. It prefers well-drained soil and likes a sunny site. Despite being the hardiest species in the genus *Phoenix*, it requires protection from excessive cold and wet, so we grow it in a large pot which can be moved into a cool, frost-free glasshouse during the winter months.

Phoenix theophrasti

Primula sieboldii Philipp Franz Balthasar von Siebold

Philipp Franz von Siebold's statue in his memorial garden in Leiden Botanic Garden

A pretty Japanese primrose named for Dr Philipp Franz Balthasar von Siebold (1796–1866), a German physician/botanist/zoologist, who worked in Japan and introduced many new plants to Europe.

His daughter Oine (1827–1903) was the first practising female physician in Japan. Siebold studied medicine at the University of Würzburg, where he qualified in 1820. He became a physician to the Dutch army in 1822 and sailed as the ship's doctor to Indonesia in 1823, from where he was sent to Dejima, Japan, where he continued as a doctor to the Dutch military. Dejima had a botanic garden and the botanists Engelbert Kaempfer and Carl Thunberg had both been resident physicians there. Siebold was an adventurer, hugely knowledgeable in the sciences of his time, and passionate about Japanese culture. He founded a school nearby at Narutaki, Nagasaki, and attracted many Japanese students both medical and botanical. He collected over 1,000 native plants for his garden, sent home *Hosta* and *Hydrangea*, and smuggled seeds of the tea plant, *Camellia sinensis*, to Java. He co-authored *Flora Japonica* (1835), *Bibliotheca Japonica* (1833–4) and *Nippon* (1832–52). He was expelled, accused of spying, in 1829 and returned to Indonesia with his collections and thence to Brussels. He settled in Leiden with his herbarium of 12,000 Japanese plants, writing his books, was rewarded and honoured by the Dutch government, and his advice on Japanese matters was sought internationally. He returned to Japan from 1859–63 as a Dutch government adviser (Hind and Kay, 2006). His impact on Dutch horticulture was, and is, immeasurable.

Primula sieboldii has no medicinal value or uses, but is a popular garden plant introduced by von Siebold from Japan, where it had long been in cultivation. ■

Primula sieboldii is a herbaceous perennial in the family Primulaceae that is distributed from eastern Siberia to Japan. The cultivars, 'Long Acre' hybrids in mixed colours and forms, grow happily in a lightly shaded border in damp, humus-rich soil amongst woodland plants. Lots of well-rotted organic matter was incorporated on planting. In spring, small spikes of star-shaped flowers appear above lush green foliage. They are mulched annually with bark chips and cut down in spring to remove old, untidy leaves and make way for new foliage. In dry spells they become dormant.

Primula sieboldii 'Long Acre' hybrid

Rohdea japonica

Rohdea japonica Michael Rohde

Michael Rohde (1782–1812) was a physician and botanist from Bremen, Germany.

He studied in Göttingen from 1800–4, initially with the aim of becoming a civil servant involved with the financial control of industry ('Cameralwissenschaften') and then qualified as a doctor. His doctoral thesis was on quinine, *Monographiae cinchonae generis tentamen* (1804). In 1804–8, Rohde travelled in southern Germany, Austria and France completing his medical training and studying botany. He exchanged letters about the flora of southern France with the French botanist Jean Loiseleur-Deslongchamps. In 1809 he started practising medicine in Bremen, but kept working enthusiastically at botany. He was close friends with the botanists AW Roth of Bremen-Vegesack, L Christian Treviranus (professor of botany in the University of Bonn) and FC Mertens (professor of botany in Bremen). Rohde died of typhoid in 1812, aged 30.

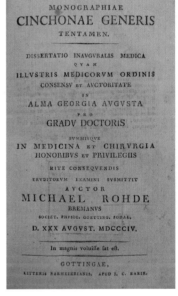

Title page of Michael Rohde's *Monographiae cinchonae generis tentamen* (1804). Image: © Royal Botanic Gardens, Kew

Rohdea japonica is a monotypic genus known as *omoto* in Japan, meaning 'evergreen'. It is regarded as a symbol of long life and good fortune; Ieyasu Tokugawa, the first Shogun of the Edo period (1603–1867), took three plants with him to Edo Castle to ensure happy fortune. Its cultivation became such a craze in Japan that its sale was banned in 1852, but it remains hugely popular, with 600 cultivars registered with the Japan Rohdea Society. It is used in Chinese medicine, but is regarded elsewhere as being poisonous and best avoided. ∎

'Its cultivation became such a craze in Japan that its sale was banned in 1852, but it remains hugely popular, with 600 cultivars registered with the Japan Rohdea Society.'

> This evergreen perennial hails from damp, wooded areas in China and Japan. It has strap-shaped, dark-green leaves and unusual green flowers in spring, followed by shiny red berries. In the Medicinal Garden it thrives in a shady, humus-rich border under other trees and shrubs from the region. It benefits from mulching annually and can be propagated by division or by seed sown under glass.

Rudbeckia fulgida var sullivantii 'Goldsturm'

Rudbeckia fulgida Olof Rudbeck

The Orange Cone Flower from North America is named for Olof Rudbeck, father (1630–1702) and son (1660–1740).

Olof Rudbeck the Elder was professor of medicine at Uppsala University and established a botanic garden there. He believed that Sweden was the original Atlantis and that Swedish was the language of Adam from which Hebrew and Latin had evolved (Rudbeck, 1675). On a more realistic note, he was the discoverer of the human lymphatic system. His son succeeded his father as professor of medicine, and botanised on an expedition to Lapland. One of his students was Carl Linnaeus (1707–88) who named the genus *Rudbeckia* after him and his father, taking it out of *Chrysanthemum*, *Aconitum* and *Doronicum*, where the genus had been variously placed before. He continued to publish some of his father's ideas on Atlantis (Rudbeck, 1733).

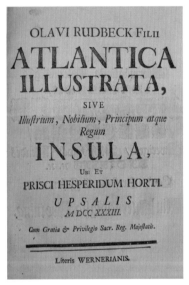

Title page of Olof Rudbeck the Younger's book on Atlantis: *Atlantica illustrata* (1733). Image: © Royal Botanic Gardens, Kew

It is a plant which is poisonous to cattle, sheep and pigs, with no medicinal uses. Daniel Austin in *Florida ethnobotany* (2004) only discusses *R. hirta*, also regarded as a toxic plant. This was used externally by the Cherokee to bathe sores and snakebites. Despite its toxicity, it was also made into a tea for treating diarrhoea; the Seminoles used it for headaches and fever and the Miccosukee for sunstroke and headache. The Cherokee and the Iroquois used it to treat intestinal worms, but it is alarming to see that it is still being recorded on internet sites as a treatment for intestinal worms in children.

We grow the variety *sullivantii* 'Goldsturm', the varietal name coming from William Starling Sullivant (1803–73), the leading expert on mosses and liverworts of his era. Rudbeckias were first described, as *Aconitum helianthemum canadense* by Cornut (1635), and *R. fulgida* was first noted in cultivation by William Aiton in his catalogue of plants at Kew in 1789. ■

> This plant from the Asteraceae family is native to the grasslands of Canada. In the Medicinal Garden it is grown amongst grasses and other American prairie plants, where it bears a profusion of golden, shuttlecock-like flowers on stiff stems in late summer. With a yearly mulch of deep well-rotted, horse manure, it is tolerant of partial shade and drought, and is disease-resistant. It can be easily propagated by seed and new plants will often flower in their first year.

Scopolia carniolica Giovanni Antonio Scopoli

Scopolia carniolica, variously called European Scopolia or Russian Belladonna, commemorates the Italian physician, botanist, geologist and chemist, Professor Giovanni Antonio Scopoli (1723–88), also known as Johann Anton Scopoli and (Latinised) as Johannes Antonius Scopolius.

He was born in Cavalese, then in the Austrian Tyrol, and completed his medical training at Innsbruck, Austria. He worked as a doctor in Cavalese and Venice, but spent time collecting plants and insects in the Alps. He worked for 16 years as physician to the mercury miners in Idrija, publishing a book on mercury poisoning in the miners, *De hydroargyro Idriensi tentamina* (1761). While there he also published *Flora Carniolica* (1760) and *Entomologia Carniolica* (1763),

Scopolia carniolica var brevifolia

on the flowers and insects of Carniola, in present-day Slovenia. He became professor of chemistry, mineralogy and metallurgy at the Mining Academy of Schemitz (now in Slovakia) from 1769–76, publishing his principles of mineralogy, *Principia mineralogiae systematicae et practicae succincte exhibentia structuram telluris* (1772). He moved to be professor of natural history (chemistry and botany) at the University of Pavia, Italy in 1777, publishing *Fundamenta chemiae praelectionibus publicis accomodata* (Fundamentals of chemicals adapted to public lectures, 1777) at the same time. The breadth of his knowledge was enormous; he published major works on world flora (*Fundamenta botanica praelectionibus publicis accomodata* (Fundamentals of botany), 1783) and fauna, translated and augmented a work on chemistry, and before his death published an account of the birds and animals collected by Pierre Sonnerat (1748–1814) during his voyages in Asia. >

'He worked ... as physician to the mercury miners in Idrija, publishing a book on mercury poisoning in the miners, *De hydroargyro Idriensi tentamina* (1761) and a textbook on mineralogy.'

Scopolia carniolica

'*Scopolia carniolica* was the first known source of scopolamine, used as a premedication prior to surgery. We grow the yellow-flowered var *brevifolia* and the brown-flowered var *carniolica*.'

He described *Digitaria sanguinalis*, Crabgrass, previously called *Panicum sanguinale* by Linnaeus, once a cultivated grain but now a pernicious weed in North America that competes with the wheat which has supplanted it, as well as describing beetles, a South American butterfly, bumble bees, salamanders and mushrooms. He was the first person to catch a live olm, *Proteus anguinus,* a blind amphibian which lives in the water of the limestone caves of southern Europe.

Scopolia carniolica was the first known source of scopolamine, used as a premedication prior to surgery. We grow the yellow-flowered var *brevifolia* and the brown-flowered var *carniolica*. Both are endangered from over-collection in the wild.

Scopolamine, like all neurotoxins, causes relaxation in small doses, progressing to disinhibition, garrulousness, incoordination, toxic confusional states with amnesia, to coma. Urban mythology holds that people who wake up during the operation, if they have had scopolamine as a premedication, are unlikely to remember the incident. This may be a 'good thing' for all concerned. ■

Scopolia carniolica in the family Solanaceae is a fully hardy, perennial herb occurring naturally in damp beech forests of the Caucasus, and central and eastern Europe. In the Medicinal Garden it thrives in shady, moist borders, where it produces attractive clumps of fresh green foliage and nodding, bell-shaped flowers in early spring. The foliage is cut down when it becomes tired and untidy, and it is mulched annually with well-rotted manure.

Scopolia carniolica illustrated in Mattioli (1569), where it was known because of its sedative properties as Solanum somniferum alterum

Serenoa repens

Serenoa repens Sereno Watson

Saw palmetto is named for Dr Sereno Watson (1820–92), a farmer's son from Connecticut who graduated from Yale in 1847.

He had no idea what to do with his life, so studied medicine at New York University, graduating in 1850, but only practising for two years (1854–6) with his elder brother Louis, in Quincy, Illinois. In 1866, he went back to Yale to study chemistry and mineralogy. He remained unsettled and, in 1867, on the spur of the moment, decided to join a surveying expedition in California, so walked across the Sierra Nevada on his own. He helped the botanist in charge, Professor WW Bailey, to collect plants and here discovered his vocation. His work was so effective that, on Professor Bailey's retirement due to illness, he became the botanist for the expedition (1868). When the expedition finished, he worked in the Gray herbarium at Harvard and published the *Catalogue of the known plants of Nevada and Utah* with 1,325 species (Watson, 1871) – a milestone in American botany. He was appointed Curator of the Gray Herbarium at Harvard in 1874, additionally looking after the botanic garden. He produced the *Bibliographic index to North American botany* (1878) and a hundred other publications, including co-authoring *Botany. Geological survey of California* (1876, 1880). He was a specialist on mosses, remembered as a shy, hard-working and infinitely diligent systematic botanist of the first rank (Coulter, 1892). He died of viral myocarditis, aged 72, following influenza (Brewer, 1903).

Serenoa repens, Saw Palmetto, is widely used as a herbal medicine for benign prostatic enlargement, despite having no clinical effect whatsoever on bladder function or prostatic size. ■

Sereno Watson in his herbarium. Image: © Royal Botanic Gardens, Kew

> *Serenoa repens* is a slow-growing, clump-forming member of the Arecaceae family. It is native to the coastal areas of south-east USA. It has blue-green, fan-shaped leaves and produces creamy, fragrant flowers and olive-like fruits. It grows well in free-draining, moist soil in sun or semi-shade. Propagation is best from seed sown under glass, as plants are difficult to re-establish after division. It is one of the hardiest palms, surviving several severe winters outside at the Medicinal Garden.

Sparmannia africana

Sparmannia africana, a large, deciduous shrub found at forest margins and in damp ravines in South Africa, is a member of the Malvaceae family. It has large heart-shaped leaves and clusters of reflexed white blooms with conspicuous, yellow and purple stamens which move when touched. As it is not hardy it grows here in a pot which is plunged into a border in summer and overwintered in a heated glasshouse during winter. Seed can be sown under glass in spring.

Doctors in the Medicinal Garden

Sparmannia africana Anders (Andreas) Sparrman

Sparmannia africana, African Hemp, is named after Dr Anders (Andreas) Sparrman (1748–1820), Swedish physician, botanist and pupil of Linnaeus.

Dr Anders Sparrman (1748–1820).
Image: © Royal College of Physicians, London

He went to Uppsala University aged nine and commenced the study of medicine at the age of 14. He travelled to and in China (1765–7) as the ship's doctor (aged 17). He published *Dissertio academica sistens iter in Chinam* (1768, A journey in China) as his student dissertation for his graduation at Uppsala. After graduating, he received a *stipendium regium* (royal scholarship) with support from Linnaeus to botanise in South Africa, where he spent much of his time as a teacher, botanising with Thunberg and a Hottentot guide when he could. When Captain Cook, in the *Resolution,* on his way to botanise in Antarctica and Tahiti, stopped in South Africa in 1772, Sparrman joined the expedition. He described it in *A voyage to the Cape of Good Hope towards the Antarctic polar circle, round the world and to the country of the Hottentots and the Caffres from the year 1772–6* (1785; 2 vols – Swedish edition in 1783). He returned to South Africa in 1775–6 and, trying to keep his medical expertise up to date, translated *Underrättelser om barn-sjukdomar och deras bote-medel* (1764) by Nicholas Rosen von Rosenstein from Swedish into English as *The diseases of children and their remedies* (1776). In his letters back to Linnaeus, he often complained of his problems in collecting.

He collected more than 1,300 botanical specimens, and between voyages worked as a professor of medicine in Uppsala, superintendent of the Cabinet of Natural Science, and a member of the Swedish Royal Academy of Science. His *Museum Carlsonianum* (1786–9) contains 100 plates of birds from all over the world. His magnificent large folio *Svensk ornithologie med efter naturen colorerade tekningar* (Swedish ornithology), published in 11 parts between 1805 and 1816, was never completed – the text stops in mid-sentence on page 44 of the last part.

African Hemp is no relation of 'hemp', as in *Cannabis sativa,* and has no medicinal or herbal use, but its hairy leaves can cause dermatitis. It has touch-sensitive flowers – a slight touch and after a second the cluster of golden stamens moves sharply outwards away from the stigma. The movements brush the pollinator and, possibly, ensure that more pollen is removed.

In 1993 an asteroid in the main asteroid belt was named Sparrman 16646 by EW Elst of the CERGA observatory in France. ■

Stokesia laevis 'Blue Star' Jonathan Stokes

DISSERTATIO
INAUGURALIS,
DE
AERE DEPHLOGISTICATO.

QUAM,
ANNUENTE SUMMO NUMINE,
Ex Auctoritate Reverendi admodum Viri,

D. GULIELMI ROBERTSON, S.S.T.P.
ACADEMIÆ EDINBURGENÆ Præfecti;

NEC NON
Amplissimi SENATUS ACADEMICI consensu,
Et nobilissimæ FACULTATIS MEDICÆ decreto,
PRO GRADU DOCTORATUS,
SUMMISQUE IN MEDICINA HONORIBUS AC PRIVILEGIIS
RITE ET LEGITIME CONSEQUENDIS
Eruditorum examini subjicit

JONATHAN STOKES,
ANGLUS.

SOC. REG. MED. EDINB. FRÆS. ANN.;
PHYS. P.A.; HIST. NAT. SOD.;
ET SOC. ANTIQ. SCOT. SOC. CORRESP.

———I here profess'd,
———and drawn empyreal air. MILT.

Ad diem 24. Junii, hora locusque folitis.

EDINBURGI:
Apud BALFOUR et SMELLIE,
Academiæ Typographos.
M,DCC,LXXXII.

The genus was named by Charles Louis L'Héritier in 1789 for Dr Jonathan Stokes (1755–1831), a member of the Lunar Society and Linnean Society, botanist and physician.

Born in Kidderminster, he qualified in medicine at the University of Edinburgh in 1782, where his academic dissertation was on dephlogisticated air *Dissertatio inauguralis de aere dephlogisticato* (1782). Prior to this time it had been believed that all inflammable materials contained an invisible matter called 'phlogiston' and, when they burnt, the phlogiston was given off and the residue was dephlogisticated and would no longer burn. It was also believed that air could only absorb a certain amount of liberated phlogiston, so something burning in a closed airspace would stop burning when the air was saturated. When oxygen was first produced artificially, it was noted that it supported combustion for longer, so this new gas was regarded as being very deficient in phlogiston, which allowed it to absorb more of the phlogiston given off by burning. It was therefore called dephlogisticated air. In 1777, Antoine Lavoisier discovered that this gas was a chemical element, to be called oxygen, which combined with inflammable substances, so debunking the phlogiston theory.

Stokes dedicated his thesis to Dr William Withering, then physician at Birmingham General Hospital and co-founder of the Lunar Society of distinguished scientists. He joined the Society in 1783, and wrote the preface to Withering's *An account of the foxglove* (1785). He also contributed histories on six patients he had treated for heart failure ('dropsy') with foxglove leaf, *Digitalis,* in his medical practice in Stourbridge. He continued at the Lunar Society until 1788, became a founding >

In the family Asteraceae, this fully hardy, herbaceous perennial is native to grasslands, wetlands and pine woods of south-eastern USA. It was introduced to England from Carolina in 1766 as *Carthamus laevis*.
In the Medicinal Garden, it helps to attract bees and butterflies at the front of a well-drained, raised bed in the partial shade of a plane tree. From July to October it bears large, white-centred, blue flowers, above evergreen rosettes of sword-shaped leaves. It appears to be disease-free and stocks can be increased easily from root cuttings in early spring. If there is time, dead heading will prolong flowering. The bed is mulched annually with well-rotted manure, taking care not to smother the plants.

Stokesia laevis 'Blue Star'

associate of the Linnean Society (1790), helped Withering with the latter's botanical works, adding a bibliography of 264 titles to the second edition of Withering's *A botanical arrangement of British plants* (1792), which much impressed Sir JE Smith, the president of the Linnean Society. He added an account of the medical uses of the plants, which Withering resented and they fell out. Stokes published his own book, a four-volume work, *A botanical materia medica: consisting of the generic and specific characters of the plants used in medicine and diet, with synonyms, and references to medical authors* (1812), and *Botanical commentaries* (1830). He corresponded with Linnaeus the younger, and Dr William Wright sent plants back to him from Jamaica. There was a Dr Jonathan Rogers Stokes who graduated from Edinburgh in 1806 with a dissertation on erysipelas, *Dissertatio medica inauguralis, de erysipelate*, and who collected plants on Snowdon at around the same era, with whom our Dr Stokes is sometimes confused.

The seeds of *Stokesia*, along with other genera within the family Asteraceae, contain vernolic acid-enriched oils which can be used as plasticisers of polyvinyl chloride, and in adhesives and paints (Perdue *et al*, 1986). ■

Sutherlandia frutescens James Sutherland

The Balloon Pea or Duck Plant was named after James Sutherland (1639–1719). He took on the care of the Trinity Hospital Garden, part of the Edinburgh University Physic Garden, in 1676.

He became regius keeper by Royal Warrant of William III in 1699. The Physic Garden had been founded in 1670 to grow medicinal plants. So, while Sutherland was not a doctor, he did look after plants for medicines and taught medical students and so I have included him. In fact he started life as the gardener and is described as 'one of those self-made men of whom Scotland has produced so many and of whom she may well be proud. ... He taught the science of herbs to the students of medicine for small fees, receiving no encouragement than a salary of £20 from the city which did not suffice to pay rent and servants' wages, to say nothing of the cost of new plants'.

When the Physic Garden was nearly washed away with the draining of the North Loch during the siege of Edinburgh Castle (1689), his plea for financial assistance was rewarded. His salary was raised to £50 and he was able to extend the Garden with purchase of land at Holyrood Palace. He was appointed as the first professor of botany in Edinburgh in 1695. Sutherland continued at Edinburgh until age 66 (1705) publishing *Hortus medicus Edinburgensis; or A catalogue of the plants in the Physical Garden at Edinburgh ...* (1683) which 'placed Edinburgh at the forefront of European botany'. His library of herbals, books on botany and numismatics (catalogue in *The Bibliotheck* 1987;14:30–106) with his collection of Greek, Roman, Scottish, Saxon and English coins and medals were purchased by the Faculty of Advocates and for many years displayed in their library (Editorial, *British Medical Journal*, 1909). >

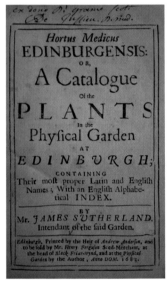

Title page of Sutherland's *Catalogue of the plants in the Physical Garden at Edinburgh*. Image: © Royal College of Physicians

'He started life as the gardener and is described as "one of those self-made men of whom Scotland has produced so many and of whom she may well be proud ".'

Sutherlandia frutescens

Sutherlandia frutescens is called the Cancer Bush in South Africa, and used for cancer and AIDS. Infusions made from the leaves are a traditional remedy for fever, chickenpox, 'flu, rheumatism, haemorrhoids, diarrhoea, and stomach and liver problems. It also makes an excellent wash for wounds. To quote a paragraph from the South African National Biodiversity Institute website:

> *It is also used to treat colds, flu, asthma, TB, bronchitis, rheumatism, rheumatoid arthritis and osteoarthritis, liver problems, hemorrhoids, piles, bladder, uterus & women's complaints, diarrhoea & dysentery, stomach ailments, heartburn, peptic ulcers, backache, diabetes, varicose veins and inflammation ... mental and emotional stress, including irritability, anxiety and depression and is used as a gentle tranquillizer. It is said to be a useful bitter tonic and that a little taken before meals will aid digestion and improve the appetite ... There is as yet no scientific support for the numerous claims and anecdotes that this plant can cure cancer.*

Historically *Sutherlandia frutescens* was first described by Jacobus Breynius in *Exoticarum aliarumque minus cognitarum plantarum centuria prima* (1678) as *Colutea aethiopica*, with red to purple flowers, grown in Amsterdam's gardens for many years, from seed collected at the Cape of Good Hope. *Colutea aethiopica* was changed by Linnaeus to *C. frutescens* in his *Hortus cliftonianus* (1738). This name had appeared in Dodoens' *Pemptades* (1583), with a woodcut, but he is describing a *Colutea* with yellow flowers which he had called *C. linsen* in his *Cruydtboeck* (1554). Neither Lyte, L'Ecluse nor Gerard's translations of Dodoens carry the name *C. frutescens*. It appeared again as *C. frutescens* in Linnaeus's definitive *Species plantarum* (1753). *Sutherlandia frutescens* stayed in the genus *Colutea* until 1812, when Robert Brown (1773-1858), working in Sir Joseph Banks' herbarium, separated it into its present genus of *Sutherlandia*. In the Medicinal Garden we grow *Colutea orientalis*, which has the same inflated, balloon-like seed pods as *Sutherlandia*, and DNA studies show them to be closely related. The earliest reference to *S. frutescens* as a cancer cure is to be found over a century ago, in the *British Medical Journal* (Editorial, 1906). ■

This is a scrambling shrub originating from dry sandy areas in South Africa. It has ferny, silvery-green foliage and bright red flowers in late summer, followed by inflated seed pods. It prefers very well-drained soil in a sunny position and can survive winter frosts if the plants are mature. Young plants are best overwintered in a heated glasshouse. It is easy to propagate from seed in spring under glass with bottom heat.

Colutea orientalis is in the sister genus to *Sutherlandia*, and carries similar inflated, balloon-like, seed pods.

Thunbergia alata

Thunbergia alata Carl Peter (Pehr or Per) Thunberg

This climbing herbaceous plant with its black-centred, golden flowers is named for Carl Peter (Pehr or Per) Thunberg (1743–1828), doctor, botanist and student of Linnaeus, who collected plants in Japan, Sri Lanka and South Africa.

Carl Peter Thunberg (1743–1828) Image: ©Royal College of Physicians

He took his degree in natural philosophy and medicine at Uppsala University in 1767, where he was a pupil of Carl Linnaeus; moving to Paris in 1770 to continue his studies. In 1771, he joined the Dutch East India Company and sailed as the ship's surgeon to Cape Town. He spent three years there learning Dutch, making three expeditions into the interior, during which he collected 3,000 plants, 1,000 of which were new to science. He sailed to Java in 1775 and thence to Dejima, Japan, the small island trading-post occupied by the Dutch and connected to the city of Nagasaki by a small bridge. He was able to travel inland, where he collected many plants. In 1776, he returned to Sweden via Sri Lanka, where he also made collecting trips. He was appointed botanical demonstrator at Uppsala in 1777 and professor of medicine and natural philosophy around 1781. He published *Flora Japonica* (1784), *Prodromus plantarum capensium* (2 vols, 1794, 1800), *Icones plantarum japonicarum* (1805), *Flora capensis* (1807–23) on the South African collections, and *Voyages de CP Thunberg au Japon par le Cap de Bonne-Espérance, les Isles de la Sonde* (1796) about his travels. He was elected a fellow of the Royal Society in April 1788.

The common name of *Thunbergia alata* is Black-Eyed Susan. It is a popular plant for window boxes and hanging baskets; it climbs like a vine to a height of up to two metres. Selective breeding has resulted in colours from red, through orange and yellow to white, some without a dark centre. However, the original plants grown as ornamentals were yellow with dark maroon centres. We also grow *Fritillaria thunbergii* and *Berberis thunbergii*. ■

This frost-tender climbing, herbaceous perennial from forest margins in tropical Africa, is a member of the family Acanthaceae with trumpet-shaped orange flowers with dark maroon centres. It is grown as a half-hardy annual in the Medicinal Garden. We sow seed under glass in spring, harden off in a cold frame and plant out on a sunny terrace after the danger of frost is past. It thrives in a large pot in a fertile, loam-based mix with a tripod as support and is well watered and fed throughout the summer. In autumn, ripe seed is collected to be sown the following year.

Tigridia pavonia

Tigridia pavonia Joseph (José) Pavón Jiménez

These colourful tulip-like flowers are named by de Candolle for Joseph (José) Pavón Jiménez (1754–1840), the Spanish pharmacist/botanist who accompanied Hipólito Ruiz and Joseph Dombey on their epic botanising in Peru and Chile (1777–88) in search of quinine and medicinal plants.

Hipólito Ruiz, who accompanied Joseph Pavón to Peru in 1777

On 8 April 1777, King Carlos III of Spain gave permission for the botanists and two artists to travel from Spain to America to study the flora of Peru and Chile, then Spanish dominions. Initially around Lima, and then further afield, they collected plants which their artists painted; they wrote descriptions and pressed herbarium specimens. Apart from a year in Chile (1782–3), about which we know little because all their specimens, diaries, descriptions and paintings for this period were destroyed in a fire, Ruiz and Pavón stayed in Peru until 31 March 1788, when they returned to Spain, landing in Cadiz on 12 September 1788. Thereafter, they spent years cataloguing their herbarium collection and preparing manuscripts for publication. The *Florae Peruvianae, et Chilensis, Prodromus* (1794), *Systema vegetabilium Florae Peruvianae et Chilensis* (1798), and *Flora Peruviana et Chilensis* (volumes 1–3, 1798–1802) were their completed works, but even before the death of Ruiz (aged 62 in 1816), the project lapsed into chaos. Pavón died in poverty in 1840 at the age of 86. Two of the remaining volumes, volume four in 1954 and volume five (part only) in 1959, were compiled from their manuscript notes. Volumes six and seven await publication.

The original name for *Tigridia pavonia* was given by Linnaeus' son as *Ferraria pavonia* in 1782, and it was de Candolle, who had access to Ruiz and Pavón's duplicate herbarium specimens, which had been sold to Aylmer Lambert in London, who reclassified it as *Tigridia* in 1802. My great-great-grandmother painted one in her garden some 20 years later (pictured overleaf). Ruiz records in his diary (Ruiz, 1940) that they found a *Ferraria* in the gorge of San Mateo de Matucaan in 1779 and in the province of Canta in 1781. >

'Pavón died in poverty in 1840 at the age of 86. Two of the remaining volumes, volume four in 1954 and volume five (part only) in 1959, were compiled from their manuscript notes.'

> '**The corms of *Tigridia pavonia* taste like sweet potato when baked, but they produce a burning sensation in the mouth if eaten raw.**'

Ruiz, while in Chile, records finding *Ferraria lagues*, a name which appears to have been published as the homophone *Ferraria lahue* (the Spanish 'g' is pronounced like an English 'h') and that the bulbs are baked or boiled and taste of hazelnuts. However, this is now in the genus *Herbertia*. Ken Fern writes in the 'Plants for a Future' website that the corms of *Tigridia pavonia* taste like sweet potato when baked, but they produce a burning sensation in the mouth if eaten raw. Sounds like he tried them! ■

Tigridia pavonia is a bulbous perennial from Mexico in the family Iridaceae. In summer, large brightly coloured, exotic looking flowers appear from dawn to dusk. Although they are thought to be frost tender, we grow it outside, where it survives and self-seeds in a gritty, well-drained sunny border, amongst other plants from arid zones.

Tigridia pavonia.
August.

Tigrida pavonia by Lady Atholl Oakeley *c.* 1821

Westringia fruticosa Johan Petter Westring

Coast Rosemary from New Zealand commemorates Dr Johan Petter Westring 1753–1833, physician to King Karl XIV of Sweden and a keen lichenologist.

He was born in Linköping, Sweden, where his father was a shoemaker. He entered the University of Uppsala in 1772, where he studied under Carl Linnaeus. In 1775, he defended his thesis *Dissertatio medica de Ledo palustri*, on *Ledum palustre*, an ericaceous shrub of northern bogs, concerning its botany, history and medicinal properties, including its use in treating leprosy in Kamtschatka. He gained his MD in 1780, following another dissertation (on sneezing), *Dissertio medica de sternutatione* (1779), and lived thereafter in Norrköping, where he became superintendent of the Himmelstalunds spa (1781) and married Gertrud Margaretha Braad (1783). He was elected to the Royal Swedish Academy of Sciences (1792), became royal physician (1794) and in 1809, the senior royal physician to King Karl XIV. He was knighted in 1822.

Westringia longifolia

Sir James Smith (1759–1828), founder and first president of the Linnean Society, was elected as a foreign member of the Royal Swedish Academy of Sciences in the same year (1792). He named the genus *Westringia* five years later, following its introduction to the English horticultural market by Lee and Kennedy of the Vineyard Nursery at Hammersmith.

He wrote *Svenska lafvarnas färghistoria …* (1805–9), a work on the making of dyes and paints from lichens which had occupied him for 15 years. His interests were in advances in medicine and natural history, and he accumulated a large library and a substantial collection of natural history objects and coins. He was a member of several scientific societies, becoming, in his later years, a member (1830) of the Royal Bachelors Club, originally a private billiards club but by then a general gentleman's club in Stockholm.

No information has been found for any medicinal use or toxicity, although horticultural suppliers note that, although called 'Cape Rosemary', it is not 'Rosemary' and should not be used for cooking. ∎

Westringia fruticosa of the family Lamiaceae is a half-hardy evergreen shrub from the coastal cliffs of eastern Australia. In the Medicinal Garden we grow *Westringia fruticosa* 'Variegata', which is smaller than the type species, has attractive green and white variegated leaves and white, faintly scented flowers. It likes a site with plenty of sunlight and water in summer and prefers dry, frost-free conditions and protection from cold winds, making it more suitable for growing in a pot in the UK.

Westringia fruticosa 'Variegata'

Zantedeschia aethiopica

Zantedeschia aethiopica Giovanni Zantedeschi

A luxuriant South African plant, with spectacular white blooms, probably commemorates Giovanni Zantedeschi (1773–1846), an Italian physician and botanist.

Zantedeschia aethiopica

Born in Molina, he studied medicine in Verona and Padua, and had his practice in Tremosine and later in Bovegno. He published *Descrizione dei funghi della provincia Bresciana* (a description of the fungi of Brescia) in 10 volumes (1820–4), a copy of which is to be found in the University of Leiden. He corresponded with the German botanist, Kurt Sprengel, who named the genus *Zantedeschia* in his honour in 1826, separating it from *Calla*, where, as *C. aethiopica*, it had been previously described by Linnaeus. He described *Betonica pradica, Campanula petraea, Laserpitium nitidum* and *Saxifraga arachnoidea*. The botanic museum in Molina is dedicated to his memory. His other publications include books (1831, 1835) on the mineral waters of Bovegno and cures effected with it. All his books are exceedingly rare.

The specific name, *aethiopica*, is used to indicate plants from Africa, usually South Africa, and not Ethiopia. Its leaves are used as a warm poultice for headaches in South African 'muthi' medicine. It has become an invasive weed in parts of Australia. It was introduced, as a greenhouse plant, to Europe in the mid-17th century as *Arum aethiopicum* (Commelin, 1697), where the long-lasting flowers are popular in flower arrangements, and for weddings and funerals – a curious combination. ■

> In the family Araceae, *Zantedeschia aethiopica* from South Africa, thrives in wetlands and along roadsides in tropical and temperate regions. We grow *Z. aethiopica* 'Crowborough', which is a hardier cultivar, in a cool, damp border and in large pots on a shady terrace where it produces white flowers from May to July and lush evergreen foliage all year round. In harsh winters the plant can be frost-damaged but will regrow, if not flower, the following year. The plants in pots are kept well-watered and given a balanced liquid feed every fortnight all summer. The border plants are mulched annually with bark chips.

Zinnia elegans cultivar